The "I Love Lucy" Quiz Book

Xas Merry
Christmas,
Elyce!

Have fun!
Love,
Norma

Other Books by Bart Andrews
The Official TV Trivia Quiz Book
The Official Movie Trivia Quiz Book
The Official TV Trivia Quiz Book #2
Lucy & Ricky & Fred & Ethel
Star Trek Quiz Book
TV or Not TV
The Science Fiction Movie Quiz Book
The TV Picture Quiz Book
Different Spokes for Different Folks
The TV Addict's Handbook
The Fabulous Fifties Quiz Book
The Official TV Trivia Quiz Book #3
Yankee Doodle Dandies
The Tolkien Quiz Book
The Super Sixties Quiz Book
The Worst TV Shows Ever
The TV Fun Book
Loving Lucy

The "I Love Lucy" Quiz Book

Bart Andrews

SAN DIEGO
A. S. BARNES & COMPANY, INC.

IN LONDON:
THE TANTIVY PRESS

First Edition
Manufactured in the United States of America

For information write to:
A.S. Barnes & Company, Inc.
P.O. Box 3051
La Jolla, California 92038

The Tantivy Press
Magdalen House
136-148 Tooley Street
London, SE1 2TT, England

Library of Congress Cataloging in Publication Data

Andrews, Bart.
  The I love Lucy quizbook.

    1. I love Lucy (Television program) — Miscellanea.
I. Title.
PN1992.77.I253A48   791.45′72   81-3577
ISBN 0-498-02566-7   AACR2

1 2 3 4 5 6 7 8 9 84 83 82 81

This book is dedicated to
Todd R. Gaulocher
1930– 1980

Acknowledgments

To the following individuals for making this book happen, my thanks: Marc deLeon, Jr., Thomas J. Watson, and my parents, who tuned in *I Love Lucy* when it premiered on October 15, 1951, and let me stay up past my bedtime to watch. Thanks also to the kind people at Viacom Enterprises for allowing me to do this book, and special thanks to Cindy and Charlie Tillinghast for "upgrading the line" and Mike Werthman for "upgrading the manuscript." All photographs were supplied by Viacom Enterprises, or were from the author's personal collection.

Introduction

If you've purchased this book, we have something in common—our love of *I Love Lucy*, the quintessential sitcom of the 1950s. So I'm happy to make your acquaintance.

For 30 years now, *I Love Lucy* has been entertaining generations of television viewers—millions of them. To many of us, "Lucy" represents TV at its best ... and funniest. Who could forget the sight of Lucy stomping grapes in a huge vat in Italy? Or the time she and Ethel got a job in a candy factory? Or Vitameatavegamin, Aunt Martha's Old-Fashioned Salad Dressing, and Lucy's frantic trip to the hospital to give birth to Little Ricky? The magic created by Lucy and her crazy cohorts will go down in history ... the history of the *human* race.

I've written lots of trivia books (on TV, the movies, *Star Trek*, *Star Wars*, Tolkien—you name it), but this has been my favorite assignment.

The book has been designed to make it easy to follow—there are special chapters (each containing five trivia questions) for every *I Love Lucy* episode, and we have tried to supply a photo for most of them to help jog your memory. Then there are several general-category chapters. There are true-false questions, multiple choices, fill-ins, questions involving the photos, and just straight trivia. Some of them are admittedly tough, but I think that makes it all the more fun. The toughest question on each episode is indicated by two hearts (❤❤) and each photo query by a single heart (❤).

Now if you're *really* into "Lucy," you'll want to know about the "We Love Lucy" fan club. It's a fabulous organization—international in scope—that's run by Tom Watson, a devoted Lucy-lover (just like us!). If you desire membership information, send a self-addressed, stamped envelope to Tom at Box 480216, Los Angeles, California 90048. And if you're interested in obtaining any of the photos in this book for your personal use, send a self-addressed, stamped envelope and $1.00 to Personality Photos, Box 50, Brooklyn, New York 11230, for a catalog.

Obviously, I hope you enjoy this collection of trivia questions. Let me hear from you (you can write to me in care of the publisher) if you'd like to see similar books done in this style. And—please—continue to enjoy "Lucy" whenever you can. You'll feel better for it!

Bart Andrews
Hollywood, California

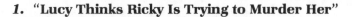

1. "Lucy Thinks Ricky Is Trying to Murder Her"

1. Name the whodunit book that prompts Lucy to think Ricky may do away with her.
   A. *The Deadly Dagger*
   B. *The Mockingbird Murder Mystery*
   C. *Who Killed the Mistress?*
2. Who are Ann, Mary, Cynthia, Alice, and Theodore?
3. Explain the line, "I got a mickey from Ricky!"
♥ 4. Lucy uses a garbage can lid to bulletproof her rear end, but what does she use to protect her chest?
♥♥ 5. Name the girl singer Ricky wants to fire.

2. "The Girls Want to Go to a Nightclub"

1. To celebrate the Mertzes' wedding anniversary, what night-club do Lucy and Ethel wish to attend?
   A. "21"
   B. The Copacabana
   C. The Stork Club
2. True or False: Ginny Jones helps Lucy and Ethel get "dates" for their evening out on the town.
❤ 3. What Spanish song does Ricky sing to Lucy and Ethel—who are disguised as country bumpkins?
4. Where does the foursome wind up spending the special occasion?
❤❤ 5. How many years have Fred and Ethel been married?

3. "Be a Pal"

1. In an effort to rekindle Ricky's interest in her, Lucy consults a book titled *How to Keep Your Honeymoon from Ending*. Who wrote this self-help manual?
   A. Dr. Harrison
   B. Dr. Marlowe
   C. Dr. Humphreys

♥ 2. After Ricky ignores Lucy at breakfast one morning, what method does she employ to regain his attention?

3. Lucy joins Ricky and Fred and their buddies in a game of _____.

4. To whose musical recording does Lucy lip-sync a Spanish song?

♥♥ 5. How many brothers does Ricky have?

1. Why does Ricky's singing partner, Joanne, decide to leave the nightclub act?
   A. She's going to have a baby
   B. She's getting married
   C. She's moving to Los Angeles
2. Butch is the name of the Mertzes' _____.
3. True or False: Ricky's piano player is named Alberto.
4. Before Lucy sings "Sally Sweet," what number does Ricky offer his Tropicana audience?
5. What size costume must Lucy be able to fit into?

5. "The Quiz Show"

♥ 1. Who is the host of the radio game show, *Females Are Fabulous?*

2. What is the program's first prize money?
   A. $1,000
   B. $500
   C. $100

3. True or False: After donning a raincoat for her radio stunt, Lucy sings "My Bonnie Lies Over the Ocean."

4. What unusual marriage-related stunt is Lucy required to do at home in order to win the big prize?

♥♥ 5. After paying all of her overdue bills, how much money is Lucy left with?

6. "The Audition"

1. For what type of show is Ricky auditioning?
   A. Television
   B. Radio
   C. Broadway

2. What famous Ricky Ricardo song is sung?

3. Dressed as "The Professor," Lucy plays what musical instrument?

4. What story twist occurs at the end, after both Lucy and Ricky perform at the Tropicana?

♥♥ 5. Name the clown who gets injured during rehearsal.

7. "The Séance"

1. Name the theatrical producer with whom Ricky is about to negotiate a deal.
   A. Mr. Meriweather
   B. Mr. Carter
   C. Mr. Perkins
2. What is the punch line to this exchange of dialogue: "I'm a one . . . I'm a five . . . I'm a three"?
3. True or False: Tillie is the producer's late wife.
♥ 4. What part does Ethel play at the séance?
♥♥ 5. What astrological sign is Lucy?

8. "Men Are Messy"

1. Publicity-minded Ricky wants to be featured in what professional magazine?
   A. *Downbeat*
   B. *Musician*
   C. *Halfbeat*
2. Who makes the decision to divide the apartment in half—Lucy or Ricky?
3. Jim White is the magazine's _____.
4. In what popular magazine of the 1950s does the story finally appear, causing much embarrassment for the Ricardos?
5. Name the Tropicana maid.

8

9. "Drafted"

1. A letter from the Defense Department demands Ricky's appearance at what New Jersey Army facility?
2. Why does Fred accompany Ricky?
   A. He drives the car
   B. He knows an appropriate vaudeville routine
   C. He sees it as a "vacation" from Ethel
3. The girls' incessant _____ causes the boys to assume that Lucy and Ethel are pregnant.
4. What happens to all of the guests who are invited to a going-away party at the Ricardo apartment?
❤❤ 5. On what night of the week is the party?

10. "The Fur Coat"

1. Why does Ricky actually rent a mink coat?
2. Assuming the fur coat is a gift from Ricky, what does Lucy do with the mink when she goes to bed?
3. How does Ricky plot to get the coat away from Lucy?
   A. He tells her he found it and must turn it over to the police
   B. He asks Fred to "steal" it when Lucy's asleep
   C. He says he borrowed it from a friend as a gag and must return it
4. True or False: Lucy schemes by buying a cheap fur coat, and "re-styling" it while Ricky watches in horror.
5. What is the mink coat worth?

11. "Jealous of Girl Singer"

1. Who is the object of Lucy's jealousy?
   A. Rosemary
   B. Cynthia
   C. Joanna
2. What is Ricky's favorite Cuban dinner?
3. True or False: Lucy finds a piece of red lace in Ricky's jacket pocket which leads her to believe he's having an affair.
4. How does Lucy manage to spy on Ricky and his "girl friend"?
5. What song does Ricky perform at the nightclub?

12. "The Adagio"

1. What type of dance is Ricky planning to stage at the Tropicana?

♥ 2. Jean Valjean Raymand, Lucy's new dance instructor, is the nephew of the woman who runs the _____.

3. Jealous of the teacher's attentions toward Lucy, Ricky plans to duel with pistols behind what famous New York landmark?
   A. Empire State Building
   B. Statue of Liberty
   C. Radio City Music Hall

4. Where does the "duel" finally occur?

♥♥ 5. How many children does the amorous Frenchman claim to have?

♥

13. "The Benefit"

1. Complete the name of Ethel's women's group—"The
   _____ East 68th Street Women's Club."
2. Hoping to cop a spot in the group's show, Lucy sings what
   song for Ethel?
   A. "Shine on Harvest Moon"
   B. "Sweet Sue"
   C. "She'll Be Comin' 'Round the Mountain"
3. What is Lucy's miniscule role in the audition song "Auf
   Wiedersehn"?
4. True or False: At the benefit show, Lucy and Ricky sing "Under
   the Bamboo Tree," interrupted by corny jokes.
♥♥ 5. What is the name of the old vaudeville act Lucy and Ricky
   perform?

♥

14. "The Amateur Hour"

1. What prompts Lucy to find a job to earn some extra money?
   A. She has used up her allowance for the month
   B. She has bought a new dress without Ricky's permission
   C. She wants to buy a birthday present for Ricky
2. Name the two Hudson twins Lucy babysits.
3. How much does the babysitting assignment pay?
♥ 4. Lucy and the twins win the $100 first prize at the amateur
   contest by singing what song?
♥♥ 5. What is the name of the group sponsoring the contest?

15. "Lucy Plays Cupid"

1. When a spinster neighbor reveals her love for a local grocer, Lucy signs on as her love advisor. Name the unmarried woman.

2. Name the groceryman who is the object of the old maid's affection.

❤ 3. What item is *not* on the menu when Lucy entertains the amorous storekeeper at dinner?
   A. Steak
   B. Tomato juice
   C. Ice cream

4. True or False: The grocer calls Lucy "Red."

❤❤ 5. Exactly how long has the spinster been carrying a torch for the grocer?

16. "Lucy's Fake Illness"

1. The three symptoms of Lucy's malady include amnesia, a reversion to childhood, and the desire to impersonate a celebrity. Name the actress that "sick" Lucy mimics.

2. Who is the "doctor" Ricky hires when he learns Lucy is playing a trick on him?
   A. Hy Averback
   B. Frank Nelson
   C. Hal March

3. What "dread" disease does the "physician" insist Lucy has?

4. Complete this line: We'll have to go in and take out your
   _____."

❤❤ 5. What is the title of the book Lucy reads, wherein she learns that she may have a complex?

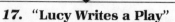

17. "Lucy Writes a Play"

1. What is the original title of Lucy's Cuban-set play?
2. True or False: Lucy changes the setting to England when Ethel has trouble effecting a Spanish accent.
♥ 3. What is the name of the revised play?
   A. *The Perils of Pamela*
   B. *Pamela's Perils*
   C. *The Perils of Pauline*
4. What role does Ethel play in both versions?
♥♥ 5. Who is to judge the women's club play competition?

18. "Break the Lease"

1. The Ricardos and Mertzes spend an evening harmonizing around the piano. What song is their favorite?

2. What actually starts the brouhaha between the two couples?

♥ 3. True or False: Lucy asks Ricky's band to play a special version of the "Mexican Hat Dance" in order to create enough havoc to break their apartment lease.

4. Where did the foursome go on vacation the summer before the argument?
   A. Maine
   B. Atlantic City
   C. Montauk Point

♥♥ 5. How much longer does the Ricardo lease have to run?

19. "The Ballet"

1. Who is Lucy's dance instructress?
   A. Madame Lamond
   B. Miss DeMille
   C. Rose DeLeon

♥ 2. When Lucy is taught the classic burlesque routine, "Slowly I Turn," by a veteran clown, what key word causes all the commotion?

3. What calamity befalls Lucy as she works out at the ballet practice bar?

4. Name the song Ricky sings at the show.

♥ ♥ 5. In what high school production does Lucy claim she played a petunia?

20. "The Young Fans"

1. True or False: The young fans are Peggy Morton and Arthur Dawson.
2. Lucy gives Arthur a dance lesson so he will be more appealing to Peggy, but something else happens. What?
3. How do the Ricardos ultimately solve the "love" problem?
4. After Ricky sings a feeble rendition of "Babalu," what does Lucy tell the youngsters?
5. How old does Lucy tell Peggy Ricky is?

20

♥

21. "New Neighbors"

1. When new tenants move into the Mertz apartment building, what does Ricky make nosy Lucy promise?
2. What is their last name?
   A. O'Brien
   B. Larabee
   C. Benson
3. What do they do for a living?
4. True or False: Lucy disguises herself as a fur coat while hiding in the new tenants' closet.
♥♥ 5. Name the policeman who has been summoned to the premises when Lucy assumes the new neighbors are spies.

♥

22. "Fred and Ethel Fight"

1. After the Mertzes argue, where does Fred move?
2. True or False: The disagreement began because Ethel called Fred's mother a weasel.
3. What does Ethel suggest that Lucy do as a sympathy ploy to win back Ricky after the Ricardos get into their own fight?
4. Besides her clothing, what does Lucy throw out of the window during a Ricky-staged "fire"?
   A. Henna rinse
   B. Jewelry
   C. Ricky's conga drum
♥♥ 5. What breaks Lucy's fall when she leaps to safety?

18

23. "The Mustache"

1. Why does Ricky grow a mustache?
♥ 2. Why does Lucy paste a beard on her face?
3. When a talent scout comes to call, how does Lucy disguise herself?
4. Does Ricky get the appropriate acting job?
♥♥ 5. Instead of spirit gum, what does Lucy use to affix her sartorial splendor?

1. After Ricky makes Lucy promise not to gossip, how does she relate to Ethel the latest "juicy tidbit"?
2. About whom is the gossip?
   A. Betty and Jack
   B. Marco Rizo
   C. Carolyn and Charlie
3. True or False: The winner of the "bet" gets breakfast in bed for one month.
♥ 4. About whom does Ricky concoct a gossipy story for Lucy's sake?
♥♥ 5. How much does Lucy pay the milkman for helping to get back at Ricky?

♥ 24

25. "Pioneer Women"

1. After Lucy and Ethel demand automatic dishwashers, what do Ricky and Fred bet the girls?
2. Lucy and Ethel yearn to belong to a women's group known as "The Society _____ League."
3. Because he is not permitted to use a taxicab, bus, or train, how does Ricky get home from the Tropicana?
   A. He walks
   B. He rides a horse
   C. He jogs
4. What do Lucy and Ethel bake that causes them some problems?
❤❤ 5. Name the two women who come to approve Lucy and Ethel for membership in their highfalutin organization.

26. "The Marriage License"

1. According to their marriage license, Lucy is married to a man named _____ _____.
2. On their way to a second ceremony, Lucy and Ricky run out of gas. Where do the Ricardos spend the night?
   A. Eagle Hotel
   B. Prospect House
   C. River Inn
3. What song is sung during the marital rites?
❤ 4. Bert Willoughby runs the town's hotel with his wife. What official political office does she hold?
❤❤ 5. Where were the Ricardos married in 1940?

27. "The Kleptomaniac"

1. Why is Lucy collecting various items and storing them in her hall closet?
2. What prized possession belonging to Fred does Ethel donate to the cause?
   A. Autographed baseball
   B. World's Fair necktie
   C. Cuckoo clock
3. What does Lucy contend she once stole from the Clyde Beatty Circus?
4. Complete this Lucy line: "I picked a peck of _____."
❤❤ 5. Name the psychiatrist whom Ricky calls in to treat Lucy's condition.

28. "Cuban Pals"

1. Lucy becomes jealous when "Little" Renita, a beautiful Spanish singer from Ricky's past, shows up. What is the senorita's last name?
2. What "colorful" song does Ricky sing at the club?
   A. "Blue Moon"
   B. "Lady in Red"
   C. "Old Black Magic"
3. Who drives Renita to the Tropicana, taking a strangely circuitous route?
4. What song does Ricky perform in full native voodoo regalia?
❤❤ 5. Who are Ricky's Cuban pals?

29. "The Freezer"

1. Who, according to Ethel, has a "big cold chest"?
   A. Her uncle
   B. Her brother
   C. Fred's brother
2. True or False: Lucy and Ethel try to get rid of the beef they bought by forcing the delivery men into taking it back.
3. Complete this Lucy Ricardo jargon: "I have sirloin, tenderloin, T-bone, rump.... Pot roast, chuck roast, ox tail _____."
❤ 4. How does Lucy get stuck in the giant walk-in freezer?
❤❤ 5. How much does the meat from Johnson's Meat Company cost the girls?

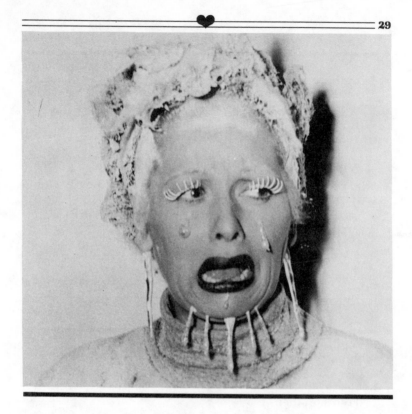

30. "Lucy Does a TV Commercial"

1. After tasting Vitameatavegamin, Lucy winces and states, "Tastes just like _____."

2. What is particularly unusual about the product?

3. Complete this line: "Are you tired, rundown, listless? Do you _____?"

4. What happens when Ricky is trying to sing his song on the *Saturday Night Variety* TV program?
   A. The camera breaks down
   B. Lucy interrupts his performance
   C. Lucy ruins the commercial

♥♥ 5. How does Lucy audition for Ricky's TV show at home?

31. "The Publicity Agent"

1. Whom does Lucy disguise herself as in an effort to boost Ricky's career?
2. Where does she take up residence?
   A. Essex House
   B. Plaza Hotel
   C. Waldorf Astoria
3. True or False: Lucy "faints" when Ricky sings "Babalu."
4. Complete this Lucy line: "I'm not a maharincess.... I'm a
   _____."
5. According to a newspaper item Lucy reads, who owns all of Benny Goodman's records?

32. "Lucy Gets Ricky on the Radio"

1. Who is the host of the *Mr. and Mrs. Quiz* show?
2. Answer this question the way Lucy does on the air: "What is the name of the animal that attaches itself to you and drains you of your blood?"
3. Answer this one like Lucy: "What is a senator's term of office?"
4. And this question: "Why did the French people place Marie Antoinette under the sharp blade of the guillotine?"
💜💜 5. What does the winner of the jackpot question receive?

33. "Lucy's Schedule"

1. Ricky's Tropicana boss is Alvin Littlefield. What is his wife's name?
2. At what hour were the Ricardos expected at the Littlefields' for dinner?
3. Ricky describes Lucy's performance while she is on a time-schedule as "jumping around like a trained _____."
💜 4. What did Mr. Littlefield find in his water glass?
    A. A penny
    B. A button
    C. A pill
💜💜 5. What kind of soup does Lucy serve at the dinner party?

---

34. "Lucy Thinks Ricky's Getting Bald"

---

1. Who runs the store which specializes in hair-restoring products and devices?
   A. Mr. Thurlough
   B. Mr. Abbott
   C. Mr. Jacobs

2. Why does Lucy plan a party for Ricky to which she invites strangers?

3. What is Fred wearing when he arrives?

4. After Lucy places a "heat cap" on Ricky's head, what does she tell him?

❤❤ 5. How much does Lucy pay each man at the party?

35. "Ricky Asks for a Raise"

1. How many other job offers does Lucy claim Ricky has received?
   A. Two
   B. Six
   C. Twelve
2. Who replaces Ricky at the Tropicana after he decides to quit?
❤ 3. Who is the Tropicana maitre d'?
4. True or False: The Mertzes borrow the wardrobe trunk, with its vast array of costumes, from Hal King.
❤❤ 5. How many tables are there at the Tropicana?

36. "The Anniversary Present"

1. Where does neighbor Grace Foster work?
   A. Joseff's Jewelry Store
   B. Maurice and Company
   C. Foster Fashions

2. Lucy and Ethel's favorite eavesdropping device, the "snooper's friend," is really a _____.

♥ 3. How does Lucy spy on Ricky and Grace?

4. What is Lucy's anniversary present?

♥♥ 5. What anniversary are the Ricardos about to celebrate?

---

37. "The Handcuffs"

1. How far back do the second set of handcuffs date?
2. What is the name of the locksmith?
   A. Mr. Johnson
   B. Mr. Andrews
   C. Mr. Walters
3. True or False: The locksmith lives in White Plains.
4. What type of hat does Ricky wear when he sings "In Santiago Chile"?
❤ ❤ 5. What is the name of the TV show Ricky is supposed to appear on?

---

38. "The Operetta"

1. What elected office does Lucy hold in her women's club?
   A. Treasurer
   B. Secretary
   C. Vice President
2. The title of the operetta is The _____Peasant.
❤ 3. Lucy plays Camille, Queen of the Gypsies, in the play, but what parts do Ricky, Fred, and Ethel portray?
4. What line follows, "I am the good Prince Lancelot"?
❤ ❤ 5. What scheme does Lucy employ to rent the costumes and scenery?

39. "Job Switching"

1. Where do the girls find employment as candymakers?
   A. Kramer's Kandy Kitchen
   B. ABC Candy Company
   C. Bon Bon Delights

2. While Lucy and Ethel are on their jobs, Ricky and Fred become "househusbands." What dinner plans do they have?

♥ 3. What happens to the girls on the assembly line in the wrapping department?

4. What "unusual" gifts do Ricky and Fred buy the wives as a truce offering?

♥♥ 5. Name the employment agency Lucy and Ethel use to find themselves jobs.

40. "The Saxophone"

 1. True or False: The only tune Lucy knows how to play on her instrument is "Sweet Sue."

2. Who teaches Lucy how to dress and act like a musician?

3. In order to make Ricky think she's having an affair, what does Lucy purposely leave around the house?

4. Where does Julie work?
   A. Musician's union
   B. Tropicana
   C. Music store

5. Where did Lucy go to high school?

41. "Vacation From Marriage"

1. According to this episode, how many years have the Mertzes been married?
   A. 18
   B. 25
   C. 20

♥ 2. Complete this Lucy line: "We are knee-deep in a _____."

3. When they realize their husbands may be wise to their schemes, where do the girls take refuge?

4. What nightclub do Lucy and Ethel claim they've been to four times in one week?

♥♥ 5. Who is Mrs. Sanders?

42. "The Courtroom"

1. On what occasion do Lucy and Ricky gives the Mertzes a new TV set?

2. When the foursome goes to court in a dispute, whom do the Ricardos retain as their lawyer?

3. What prompts Fred to chastise Ethel about hurting their chances of winning the case?

4. What happens to the judge's TV set during the course of the trial?

5. How big is the screen on the Mertzes' new television?

43. "Redecorating"

1. Name the major furniture exhibit being held in town which Lucy and Ethel attend.
2. Whose musicial comedy does Ricky have tickets for?
3. Who is the secondhand furniture dealer?
   A. Dan Jenkins
   B. Jake Daniels
   C. Mac McNeil
4. What does Lucy do with the money she is paid for her old furnishings?
5. How much does the dealer give Lucy for the furniture?

44. "Ricky Loses His Voice"

1. Unable to talk because of laryngitis, how does Ricky manage to communicate with Lucy?

♥ 2. What old vaudeville act will Lucy, self-appointed Tropicana producer, stage at the club?

3. When Lucy looks down Ricky's "colorful" throat, what does she liken the sight to?

4. What song do Fred and Ethel sing in the show?
   A. "Nothin' Could Be Finer Than to Be in Carolina"
   B. "Has Anybody Seen My Gal?"
   C. "Tea for Two"

♥ ♥ 5. Who is the new owner of the Tropicana?

45. "Sales Resistance"

1. From whom does Lucy buy a kitchen gadget for $7.98?
   A. Harry Martin
   B. Jack Lacey
   C. Wally Pearson

2. What company does the salesman represent?

❤ 3. Complete this Lucy line, delivered after she unsuccessfully tries to sell off the vacuum cleaner: "One more hour and _____."

4. True or False: With his "sales resistance" low, Fred buys Ethel a new refrigerator.

❤❤ 5. What new song does Ricky sing while the Mertzes look on?

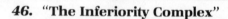

46. "The Inferiority Complex"

1. True or False: Lucy first manifests her so-called complex when no one laughs at her joke.
2. What name does the psychiatrist use when, at Ricky's request, he visits the Ricardos' apartment?
   A. Bob Stewart
   B. Jack Stewart
   C. Chuck Stewart
3. Why does Ricky decide to dismiss the doctor?
4. Complete this Lucy line: "The next thing you know you'll want me to _____."
♥♥ 5. Name the psychiatrist.

47. "The Club Election"

♥ 1. When Lucy is not nominated for the club's presidency, how does she bribe a certain fellow club member?

2. When Lucy and Ethel are pitted against each other in the election, what do Fred and Ricky do to counteract their wives' campaigning?
   A. They ignore their wives
   B. They hide their campaign signs
   C. They try to influence the deciding vote

3. True or False: The deciding vote belongs to Ruth Knickerbocker.

4. Who wins the presidency?

♥♥ 5. Before her name became Caroline, Mrs. Appleby had a different first name. Can you recall it?

♥

48. "The Black Eye"

1. How does Lucy get her black eye?
2. Using Ricky's name and hoping to patch up a "disagreement" Lucy and Ricky are supposedly having, what does Fred attempt to do?
   A. Send Lucy flowers
   B. Send Lucy candy
   C. Send Lucy flowers and candy
3. Fred gets *his* black eye when Ethel hits him with a _____.
4. True or False: Ricky gets *his* shiner when Lucy slugs him.
♥♥ 5. Name the main characters in the murder mystery Lucy and Ricky are reading.

♥

49. "Lucy Changes Her Mind"

1. What does Lucy first order at the restaurant?
   A. Pork chops
   B. Roast beef
   C. Steak
2. Besides changing her meal order, what does Lucy change?
♥ 3. Lucy's old beau now owns Henderson's Furs, a swanky fur salon. What is Henderson's first name?
4. True or False: Henderson's older brother is named George.
♥♥ 5. Aside from his thick eyeglasses, what characteristic can you recall about the waiter?

40

HENDERSON'S FURS

50. "Lucy Is Enceinte"

1. Who is the first person to assume that Lucy is pregnant?
2. What does Fred purchase for his unborn godchild?
   A. Baseball
   B. Baseball bat
   C. Both
3. After a few futile attempts, how does Lucy finally reveal the baby news to Ricky?
♥ 4. What song does hubby sing to his wife at the Tropicana?
♥♥ 5. What word, introduced by her grandmother, does Lucy use to describe the way she feels?

51. "Pregnant Women"

1. How does Ricky react about the choice of names for the baby when Lucy says, "I want the names to be unique and euphonious"?

2. What does Ricky attempt to make for Lucy's breakfast, causing Lucy to tell Ethel, "He said the charcoal would be good for the baby's teeth"?

3. Of Gregory and Joanne, John and Mary, Anthony and Cleopatra, and Robert and Madelyn, which pair of names does Lucy *not* consider as possibilities?

4. True or False: Lucy feels rejected when Ricky begins buying gifts for the unborn baby.

❤ ❤ 5. What song does Ricky sing to Lucy at the Tropicana, claiming that it is their favorite song?

52. "Lucy's Show Biz Swan Song"

1. What song do Fred and Ethel offer as a pre-audition for Ricky's "Gay Nineties" revue?
♥ 2. Name the clown who auditions for Ricky.
   A. Buffo
   B. Pepino
   C. Pepito
3. Lucy and Ethel call their "act" _____ and Mertz.
4. What song is sung by the barbershop quartet?
♥ ♥ 5. Whom does Lucy replace in the barbershop quartet?

53. "Lucy Hires an English Tutor"

1. The tutor's name is Percy _____.

❤ 2. What song does the teacher wish to introduce at Ricky's club?

3. True or False: In lieu of permitting the tutor to sing the song at the club, Ricky offers to show the song to some record companies.

4. How does Ricky, annoyed at Lucy, get even with her?

❤❤ 5. What three words does the tutor implore his four students to rid from their speech?

54. "Ricky Has Labor Pains"

1. Who gives Lucy a baby shower?
2. Ricky's sickness symptoms are nausea, dizzy spells, and
   _____.
♥ 3. What unique idea do Lucy and Ethel concoct to make Ricky the center of attention?
4. What does Lucy like her pistachio ice cream covered with?
   A. Pickles
   B. Sardines
   C. Olives
♥♥ 5. In what month of pregnancy is Lucy?

55. "Lucy Becomes a Sculptress"

1. True or False: The owner of the art supply store is George Abbott.
2. Who becomes Lucy's first model?
   A. Ricky
   B. Ethel
   C. Fred
3. What is Lucy's *ultimate* effort?
4. *Times* critic Harvey offers $_____ for the piece.
5. How much modeling clay does Lucy purchase?

56. "Lucy Goes to the Hospital"

1. Who is Lucy's doctor?
   A. Dr. Harris
   B. Dr. Parker
   C. Dr. Williams
2. The other occupant of the father's waiting room at the hospital is Mr. _____.
3. What type of musical number is Ricky performing at his club later that night?
4. What is Ricky's reaction upon seeing his newborn son?
❤❤ 5. Once at the hospital, how much time does Ricky have before he must leave for the Tropicana?

57. "No Children Allowed"

1. Name the apartment house tenant most annoyed by Little Ricky's nocturnal wailing?
   A. Mrs. Benson
   B. Mrs. Trumbull
   C. Miss Lewis
❤ 2. Complete this Ethel Mertz phrase: "My friendship with the Ricardos means more to me than _____."
3. True or False: Lucy later claims, "That speech has had more performances than *Oklahoma!*"
4. After patching up their disagreement, with whom do the Ricardos and Mertzes find Little Ricky?
❤❤ 5. How many ladies, aside from Lucy and Ethel, show up for the bridge game?

58. "Lucy Hires a Maid"

1. Name the maid.
   A. Mrs. Porter
   B. Bertha
   C. Josephine

2. What does she insist upon when she learns that the Ricardos have an infant?

3. What scheme do Lucy and Ethel dream up to get rid of the bossy servant?

♥ 4. True or False: Fred finally fires the maid.

♥♥ 5. What does the maid eat for lunch?

59. "The Indian Show"

1. Complete the title of the book Lucy is reading—*Blood Curdling* _____.

2. Why does Ricky assume that Lucy's show business aspirations are finally over?

❤ 3. What is the name of the musical number Lucy finally weedles her way into?
   A. "The Waters of the Minnetonka"
   B. "Indian Love Call"
   C. "Three Little Indians"

4. True or False: While Lucy is performing, Ethel is watching Little Ricky.

❤❤ 5. Who is Ricky's regular girl singer?

♥

60. "Lucy's Last Birthday"

1. What does Mrs. Trumbull do when she learns that it is Lucy's birthday?
2. What is the name of the Salvation Army-type group that Lucy joins?
3. Fill in the three missing words in this oration: "I was just a bit of flotsam in the sea. A pitiful outcast, shunned by _____."
4. What does Ricky give Lucy as a birthday gift?
   A. A mink stole
   B. A diamond bracelet
   C. A song
♥♥ 5. What ruse does Ricky use to get Lucy down to the Tropicana?

61. "The Ricardos Change Apartments"

1. With an extra member in the family, the Ricardos need more room. Whose larger apartment does Lucy wish to occupy?

2. What is the number of the new residence?
   A. 3-B
   B. 3-C
   C. 3-D

3. True or False: The former tenants require less space because their daughter has married.

❤ 4. How does Lucy attempt to convince Ricky that they need a larger apartment?

❤❤ 5. How much more rent per month is the new flat?

62. "Lucy Is Matchmaker"

1. True or False: Eddie Grant, the object of Lucy's matchmaking, is a friend of Ricky's.
2. The bachelor is a _____ salesman.
3. Name Lucy's man-chasing girl friend.
   - A. Grace Munsen
   - B. Hazel Pierce
   - C. Sylvia Collins
♥ 4. Who is peering over Lucy's shoulder?
♥♥ 5. What is Eddie Grant's hotel room number?

♥

63. "Lucy Wants New Furniture"

1. How much does Lucy's new sofa and coffee table cost?
   A. $199
   B. $299
   C. $399
2. What does she use as a down payment?
3. Presuming Ricky will be upset by her spending spree, where does Lucy hide the new furnishings?
4. After eyeing Lucy's home permanent, what does Fred exclaim? "Well, if it isn't _____!"
♥♥ 5. Lucy needs a new dress to attend a special party at the Tropicana. Who is hosting this bash?

♥

64. "The Camping Trip"

1. What section of the newspaper does Lucy suddenly start reading?
2. What type of hunting does Lucy intend to do?
   A. Duck
   B. Geese
   C. Deer
3. How does Ethel assist Lucy on the camping trip?
♥ 4. True or False: Lucy washes her hair with the water in her canteen.
♥♥ 5. According to a newspaper account Lucy reads, where are they "racing little girls"?

65. "Ricky's *Life* Story"

1. What part of Lucy's anatomy is visible in a photo in the *Life* magazine article about Ricky—her left or right elbow?
♥ 2. What type of dance routine does Ricky suggest for Lucy's act at the club?
3. Finally, what part does Lucy play in Ricky's act?
4. Which song does Ricky *not* perform?
   A. "Lady of Spain"
   B. "The Loveliest Night of the Year"
   C. "Spanish Eyes"
♥♥ 5. How long does Lucy rehearse for her possible dance performance?

66. "Ricky and Fred Are TV Fans"

1. What are Ricky and Fred watching on television?
2. What touches off Lucy's brush with the law?
   A. She accidentally trespasses on someone's property
   B. She mistakenly picks up the wrong handbag
   C. She tries to make her own change from a restaurant cash register
3. True or False: Lucy and Ethel are arrested atop the Mertz apartment building.
4. Lucy and Ethel are accused by the police of being Pickpocket Pearl and Sticky Fingers Sal. Which one is "Lucy"?
❤❤ 5. Name the precinct sergeant.

67. "Never Do Business with Friends"

1. For how much do the Ricardos sell their old washing machine to the Mertzes?
   A. $25
   B. $35
   C. $50
2. True or False: The appliance repairman is willing to pay $75 for the washer in its present condition.
3. Where is the washer tug-o-war between the Ricardos and Mertzes held?
4. What ultimately happens to the washer?
❤❤ 5. Name Mrs. Trumbull's nephew, the repairman.

68. "The Girls Go Into Business"

1. Name the dress shop Lucy and Ethel buy.
❤ 2. What is the owner's original asking price?
   A. $1,000
   B. $2,000
   C. $3,000
3. Scheming to cover her financial tracks, what does Lucy ask Ricky to say on the telephone in Spanish? "The _____ is good."
4. What is the ultimate value of the store and why?
❤❤ 5. How many sales do Lucy and Ethel make on their first day in business?

69. "Lucy and Ethel Buy the Same Dress"

1. Who will host the "annual" Wednesday Afternoon Fine Arts League talent show?
2. Name the Cole Porter tune Lucy and Ethel sing.
♥ 3. True or False: Lucy buys her gown at Macy's.
4. Complete this Lucy line: "Next to sugar, Cuba's biggest export is _____."
♥♥ 5. When does the talent show air?

♥

70. "Equal Rights"

1. Name the type of restaurant the Ricardos and Mertzes frequent.
   A. Italian
   B. French
   C. Cuban

2. When the girls do not have money to pay their own checks, what happens?

3. True or False: Lucy and Ethel lure Ricky and Fred back to the restaurant by claiming they're being assaulted by thugs.

4. Who winds up in jail?

♥♥ 5. What does Ricky call the waiter?

71. "Baby Pictures"

❤ 1. Who is older—Little Ricky or little Stevie Appleby?

2. What does Charlie Appleby do for a living?
   A. Executive at an ad agency
   B. Runs a TV station
   C. TV announcer

3. Charlie claims that _____ and Conway Tearle will become big television stars.

4. What song does Ricky sing on the TV show?

❤❤ 5. How old is Little Ricky?

72. "Lucy Tells the Truth"

1. Ricky, Fred, and Ethel make a $100 bet with Lucy that she can't go _____ hours without telling a lie.
♥ 2. What style of new furniture has Caroline Appleby recently acquired?
3. With honesty her best policy, what does Lucy call Fred?
   A. Miser
   B. Penny-pincher
   C. Tightwad
4. In this episode and subsequent ones, what is the Ricardos' apartment number?
♥♥ 5. Name the knife-thrower at the TV show audition.

73. "The French Revue"

1. What does Lucy promise the French waiter in return for free language lessons?
♥ 2. After Ricky forbids his wife to come near the club, how does Lucy disguise herself?
3. How does Lucy *finally* gain admittance to the Tropicana?
4. Name the tune the chorus girls and Lucy render with Ricky.
   A. "Valentine"
   B. "Alouette"
   C. "I Like Paris"
♥♥ 5. Name the French waiter.

73

61

74. "Redecorating the Mertzes' Apartment"

♥ 1. What gift is Lucy finally about to receive from Ricky?
   A. Mink stole
   B. Pearl necklace
   C. Diamond ring

2. In what unique way does Lucy inform Ethel of the impending gift?

3. What does Lucy call the proposed refurbishing session?

4. What favorite Fred Mertz possession does Lucy ruin in the process of redecorating his apartment?

♥♥ 5. What specific reason is given for redecorating the Mertzes' apartment?

75. "Too Many Crooks"

1. Who informs Ethel that Lucy has been acting suspiciously?
   A. Fred
   B. Mrs. Trumbull
   C. Ricky

♥ 2. Name the "crook" who has been menacing the neighborhood—Madame _____.

3. Assuming that Ethel is the criminal, how does Lucy hope to get Ethel's fingerprints?

4. True or False: Lucy spots Ethel on the fire escape wearing Fred's hat and coat.

♥♥ 5. What do the Ricardos decide to give Fred Mertz for his birthday?

76. "Changing the Boys' Wardrobe"

1. Whose new movie do the Ricardos and Mertzes attend?
   A. Grace Kelly's
   B. Marilyn Monroe's
   C. Lana Turner's

2. Name the year on Fred's Golden Gloves sweater.

♥ 3. True or False: After buying back their old clothing, Ricky and Fred use boxes from Saks Fifth Avenue.

4. How does Fred pass himself off when Ricky is named "one of the ten best-dressed men"?

♥♥ 5. To whom do the girls sell the boys' old clothing?

77. "Lucy Has Her Eyes Examined"

1. Ricky brings home a motion picture producer one night, a Mr. Parker. What's Mr. Parker's first name?
   A. Bill
   B. Steve
   C. Bob
2. Whom does Lucy hire to teach her the "jitterbug"?
♥ 3. What song and dance do the Mertzes perform at the audition for Parker?
4. Complete this pertinent *Variety* headline: "PARKER PREPS PROD FOR _____ PREEM."
♥♥ 5. What movie musical is Parker casting?

78. "Ricky's Old Girl Friend"

1. Complete the title of the magazine article that sets off a tiff between Lucy and Ricky—"How to Rate Your Marriage, or _____?"

♥ 2. What is Carlotta's last name?

3. Name the act in which Ricky appeared with Carlotta back in Cuba.

4. Which of the following is *not* one of Lucy's so-called old boyfriends?
   A. Billy
   B. Jerry
   C. Larry

♥ ♥ 5. Where in New York is Carlotta appearing?

78

79. "The Million-Dollar Idea"

1. What does Lucy call her million-dollar salad preparation?
2. In order to appear on a TV show at the station operated by Charlie Appleby, Lucy agrees to pay Caroline what commission?
3. Ethel portrays _____ on the commercials.
4. What is the retail price of the salad dressing per jar?
   A. 35¢
   B. 40¢
   C. 45¢
♥♥ 5. Name the host of the morning TV show on which Lucy and Ethel appear.

80. "Ricky Minds the Baby"

♥ 1. What fairy tale does Ricky tell Little Ricky?
   A. *Hansel and Gretel*
   B. *Little Red Riding Hood*
   C. *Snow White and the Seven Dwarfs*
2. When Little Ricky wanders off, what is his father doing?
3. What excuse does Ricky offer Lucy for Little Ricky's disappearance?
4. True or False: Ethel finally sneaks Little Ricky back into his crib.
♥♥ 5. The following morning, what does Ricky eat while Little Ricky has cereal?

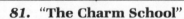

81. "The Charm School"

1. At the Ricardos' get-together, who is Tom Williams' date?
   A. Eve Whitney
   B. Marlene Saunders
   C. Jo Stafford
2. Name the school in which Lucy and Ethel enroll.
3. Fred's response when Ethel walks in and Ricky exclaims, "Who's that?" is "_____?"
4. Describe Ethel's outlandish outfit.
♥ ♥ 5. What are the girls' exact charm school test scores?

82. "Sentimental Anniversary"

1. How many years have the Ricardos been married?
   A. 12
   B. 13
   C. 14
2. What expensive gift does Ricky buy Lucy?
3. True or False: Lucy buys Ricky a new conga drum.
4. Where do the Ricardos spend their anniversary?
❤❤ 5. What excuse does Lucy give Ethel when the Mertzes inquire about their plans for the evening?

83. "Fan Magazine Interview"

❤ 1. Name the magazine writer who comes to call on the Ricardos:_____Harris.
2. What does Ethel wish to borrow when she conveniently drops in that morning?
   A. Sugar
   B. Half 'n' half
   C. An egg
3. What scheme does Jerry hatch to drum up nightclub business?
4. To whom was the sample invitation that Lucy finds in Ricky's coat pocket inscribed?
❤❤ 5. How many people are on the Tropicana mailing list?

84. "Oil Wells"

1. Name Texas oilman Sam Johnson's wife.
2. What is the original cost of the oil stock per share?
   A. $100
   B. $75
   C. $120
3. What is the color of the Cadillac Ricky intends to buy with his expected "windfall"?
♥ 4. How does Lucy plan to get her and the Mertzes' money back from Johnson?
♥♥ 5. Who is Fred's detective friend?

85. "Ricky Loses His Temper"

1. Why does Ricky lose his temper this time?
2. What type of act is Ricky negotiating for by telephone?
   A. Ventriloquism
   B. Acrobatic
   C. Musical
3. The new hat Lucy buys at the Jeri Hat Salon is a turquoise cocktail hat with _____.
❤ 4. What is inside the trick drinking glass Ricky uses?
❤❤ 5. What is Lucy and Ricky's wager?

86. "Home Movies"

1. What do the Mertzes do when Ricky shows his home movies?
2. What genre of film do Lucy and the Mertzes produce themselves which is later spliced into Ricky's TV show?
3. Name the TV producer.
   A. Bennett White
   B. Bennett Black
   C. Bennett Green
4. What Spanish song does Ricky sing in his pilot?
❤ ❤ 5. What is the title of Ricky's sample film?

87. "Bonus Bucks"

1. How much is the "bonus buck" worth?
   A. $300
   B. $500
   C. $1,000
2. Who originally finds the lucky dollar?
3. True or False: The Ricardos' half of the bill winds up at a laundry because Lucy forgets to remove it from the pocket of her robe.
4. Lucy and her 50 cents' worth of the lucky dollar wind up in the laundry's _____.
♥ ♥ 5. Name the laundry.

88. "Ricky's Hawaiian Vacation"

1. What is the actual purpose of the Hawaiian trip?
2. Name the TV game show on which Lucy is a contestant—*Be a Good* _____.
3. Who is the host of the program?
4. What other "role" does Lucy play?
   A. Fred's mother
   B. Ethel's mother
   C. Ricky's mother
♥ ♥ 5. On the TV show, Lucy is bombarded with what six items?

89. "Lucy Is Envious"

1. How much money does Lucy pledge to a charity?
   A. $250
   B. $500
   C. $1,000
2. How much does Ethel promise to contribute—$250 or $500?
3. Name the film for which Lucy and Ethel perform a publicity stunt.
♥ 4. Where does the stunt take place?
♥ ♥ 5. Who is Lucy's highfalutin friend?

90. "Lucy Writes a Novel"

1. What prompts Lucy to start writing a book?
   A. She wants to get her life story down on paper
   B. She read about a housewife who made a fortune writing a book
   C. She wants Little Ricky to have *two* famous parents
2. What does Lucy title her masterpiece:_____*Gone with the Wind*.
❤ 3. What name does the "Ethel Mertz" character go by?
4. After burning the manuscript, what title does Ethel wish to bestow on the work?
❤❤ 5. What publisher offers Lucy a $100 advance?

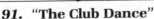

91. "The Club Dance"

♥ 1. Why do Lucy and her Wednesday Afternoon Fine Arts League cronies decide to form the all-girl orchestra?
   A. They want to prove to Ricky they can play as well as his musicians
   B. They hope to raise money for the club
   C. They made a bet with the owner of the Tropicana

2. Who comments, "When Lucy plays the saxophone, it sounds like a moose with a head cold"?

3. True or False: Lucy forces her way into the band by bribing Caroline.

4. What is the group's big musical number?

♥♥ 5. How many members of Ricky's band join the club group for their appearance?

92. "The Diner"

1. Name the restaurant the Ricardos and Mertzes buy.
   A. Bill's Place
   B. Harry's Diner
   C. Lexington Grille
2. The foursome pays $_____ for the eatery.
3. Based on Ricky's drawing power, what *new* name do they originally bestow on the diner?
4. True or False: When a drunk shows up, pie gets a sudden price reduction.
❤ ❤ 5. To whom do they sell the diner?

93. "The Black Wig"

1. What type of stylish haircut is Lucy anxious to acquire?
2. Who is her hairdresser?
   A. Roberta
   B. Irma
   C. Louie
3. Where do Lucy and Ethel plan to meet Ricky and Fred for dinner?
4. Name the three types of costumes Ethel wears on the blind date—Eskimo, American Indian, and _____.
5. From whom does Ethel borrow her various outfits?

94. "Tennessee Ernie Visits"

1. In her letter, what does Lucy's mother call Ricky?

♥ 2. Complete Mrs. MacGillicuddy's description of Ernie Ford—"A friend's roommate's cousin's _____."

3. What is unusual about the way Ernie sleeps on the Mertzes' rollaway bed?

4. What type of women did Ernie's mother warn him about before he left Bent Fork?
   A. "Vampy women"
   B. "Wicked city women"
   C. "Street women"

♥♥ 5. What song does Ernie sing with his guitar in the early morning hours?

♥ 94

95. "Tennessee Ernie Hangs On"

1. What "sure-fire" scheme do the Ricardos first hatch to get Ernie to go back to Bent Fork? (Clue: it has something to do with a bus ticket.)

2. When that backfires, what domestic plan of action is put into effect?

3. Name the variety show on which Ernie and our foursome appear in order to win the money for his trip home— *Millikan's* _____ *Hour*.

4. What song do they sing?
   A. "Home on the Range"
   B. "Birmingham Jail"
   C. "Ya'll Come to Meet Us When You Can"

5. How do they bill themselves for the TV show?

96. "The Golf Game"

1. Name the sport Lucy and Ethel take up in the Ricardo living room.

2. What golf pro do the girls meet on the links?

3. True or False: Ricky and Fred try to discourage the girls from taking up golf by inventing their own, unique set of rules.

4. How do the girls retaliate at the National Golf Day championship tournament?
   A. They replace the golf balls with ping-pong balls
   B. They fill up the holes with dirt
   C. They sign on as caddies and give the boys a taste of their own medicine

 5. Who is the famous American used as an example of a non-golf-playing wife?

96

1. In what New England state has Ricky's band been booked for the summer?
2. True or False: The real estate saleslady who attempts to sublet the Ricardo apartment is named Mrs. Hawthorne.
3. How much is the Ricardos' rent for Apartment 3-D?
   A. $125 per month
   B. $150 per month
   C. $175 per month
♥ 4. Prissy Mr. Beecher finally sublets the apartment. Why is he so nervous?
♥♥ 5. After the New England booking is canceled, where is the band scheduled to appear?

♥ ══════ 97

98. "Lucy Cries Wolf"

1. What is the essence of the newspaper article that prompts Lucy's paranoia?

2. Jokingly, Ricky assures Lucy he would rush home from the Tropicana if she were in trouble "right between the _____ and the _____."

♥ 3. After Lucy cries wolf once too often, climbing out on a ledge for effect, what do Ricky and the Mertzes do?

4. Later on, what happens to Lucy while Ricky, Fred, and Ethel are playing cards?
   A. She decides to stay overnight with Mrs. Trumbull
   B. She is accosted by thugs
   C. She plays a game of solitaire

♥♥ 5. What is Ethel's retort when Ricky says she can have all of Lucy's clothes?

99. "The Matchmaker"

1. To make a good impression on the Ricardos' unmarried friends, Dorothy and Sam, Lucy decides to prepare a special meal. What is it?
   A. Roast beef
   B. Chicken
   C. Pot roast

2. Why does Ricky decide to go to bed early the night of the dinner party?

3. True or False: The actor who portrays Sam is Frank Nelson.

4. What eventually happens to Sam and Dorothy?

5. What are Sam and Dorothy's last names?

100. "The Business Manager"

1. What is the business manager's name?
   A. Hickox
   B. Hundley
   C. Hinkley

♥ 2. After being put on a strict budget, how does Lucy scheme to earn some extra cash?

3. Ricky believes that Lucy is playing the stock market when he sees a note saying, "Buy can _____."

4. How much money does Ricky make in the market?

♥♥ 5. After paying all of her past obligations at the accountant's insistence, how much money is Lucy left with?

100

101. "Mr. and Mrs. TV Show"

1. What is the Ricardos' informal morning TV show to be called?
2. On the air, Lucy complains of a backache because she _____ on a Phipps' _____.
3. Complete this Lucy line: "Food always taste different when they fix it. I...
   A. don't know what they do to it."
   B. can't stand it."
   C. think they enjoy burning everything, even coffee."
4. When Lucy sings it, what is the climactic last line of the Phipps' theme song?
5. Name the advertising agency that represents the Phipps Department Store.

♥

102. "Mertz and Kurtz"

1. What is Fred's ex-vaudeville partner Kurtz's first name?
2. To help out the Mertzes, Lucy poses as Bessie. Who is Bessie supposed to be?
3. True or False: Kurtz is now a plumber in the Bronx.
4. What type of show does the group put on at the Tropicana to impress Kurtz's grandson?
   A. Atlantic City
   B. Gay Nineties
   C. Roaring Twenties
♥♥ 5. How was the old Mertz and Kurtz act billed?

♥

103. "Ricky's Movie Offer"

1. What is talent scout Benjamin's first name?
   A. Charles
   B. Ben
   C. Clifford
2. True or False: Lucy smashes a vase over his head because she thinks he's a prowler.
♥ 3. Lucy impersonates Marilyn Monroe, but how does Fred dress up for the audition?
4. Where does Ricky read a scene from the *Don Juan* script for the talent scout?
♥♥ 5. Who plans to audition for Benjamin as a trumpet player?

104. "Ricky's Screen Test"

1. What shape swimming pool does Lucy want when the Ricardos move to California?
   A. Heart
   B. Conga drum
   C. Cuba

2. Can you name at least three actresses who are being considered as Ricky's leading ladies in his film, *Don Juan*?

3. What screen-test line comes after, "Hark! Do I hear a foot fall?"

4. According to Ricky, Lucy's chief function at the screen test is to "_____ me the lines."

❤❤ 5. What will be the budget of *Don Juan*?

105. "Lucy's Mother-in-Law"

1. When Ricky's mother arrives for a visit, what is Lucy doing?
   A. Cleaning
   B. Cooking
   C. Ironing
2. What special dish does Lucy try to create for her in-law?—
   Arroz con _____.
3. True or False: The "mind-reader" Lucy hires to help her speak Spanish leaves suddenly because he has just learned he is a father.
4. Where does Lucy manage to lose her mother-in-law?
❤❤ 5. What is the name of the "psychic"?

106. "Ethel's Birthday"

1. On behalf of Fred, what gift does Lucy pick out for Ethel?
2. What does Ethel *really* want?
   A. Electric can opener
   B. Toaster
   C. Steam iron
3. The play to which the foursome goes to celebrate Ethel's birthday is *Over the* _____.
❤ 4. How do Lucy and Ethel settle their disagreement?
❤❤ 5. Complete this heated Lucy line: "Happy birthday, Mrs. Mertz, and I hope you live another _____!"

107. "Ricky's Contract"

1. Unnerved because he hasn't heard from Hollywood about his screen test yet, Ricky forbids Lucy to do something. What?
2. Who writes the fake telephone message that causes all the concern?
3. Where does Ricky take his band members to celebrate the news that he has won the part of Don Juan?
   A. Sardi's
   B. Lindy's
   C. The Copacabana
4. How does Lucy explain to Ricky that she received the news before he did? "A _____ told me."
❤❤ 5. How long has Ricky been waiting for the decision about his screen test to come from Hollywood?

108. "Getting Ready"

1. Which method of getting to Hollywood does Ricky *not* offer Lucy?
   A. Automobile
   B. Bus
   C. Train
2. Ethel once visited the Mayo Brothers' clinic to have her _____ removed.
❤ 3. What make of car does Fred buy for the trip west?
4. True or False: Fred pays $300 for the automobile.
❤❤ 5. Where is the used-car lot located?

109. "Lucy Learns to Drive"

1. What make and model of car does Ricky buy for the trek to California?

2. When learning how to drive, where does Lucy attempt a U-turn?
   A. Lincoln Tunnel
   B. Holland Tunnel
   C. Fifth Avenue

3. Who teaches Ethel how to drive?

♥ 4. After the two cars lock bumpers, how does Lucy get them apart?

♥♥ 5. What special assignment regarding the new car does Ricky give to Lucy before going to the club?

110. "California, Here We Come!"

1. By what other name does Lucy's mother, Mrs. MacGillicuddy, call Ricky?
2. Why do the Mertzes decide not to go to California?
♥ 3. Complete this Ethel Mertz line: "I could have done better with a _____."
4. The "extra baggage" problem is solved when Ricky suggests they send it by _____.
♥♥ 5. What is the scheduled hour of departure?

111. "First Stop"

1. Enroute, the foursome encounters signs advertising pecan pralines. Whose specialty are they? Aunt _____'s.
2. Near what big Ohio city is the rundown cafe?
   A. Cincinnati
   B. Cleveland
   C. Columbus
3. What is the "specialty of the house" on the cafe menu?
❤ 4. True or False: The "movable" motel room costs $16 per night.
❤❤ 5. Name the owner of the infamous establishment.

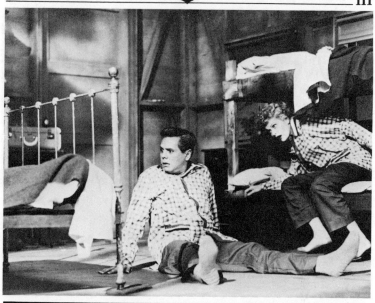

---

112. "Tennessee Bound"

1. Why is the group stopped by the sheriff?
2. Where in Tennessee are they nabbed?
❤ 3. Name the sheriff's twin daughters.
4. What song does Cousin Ernie sing?
   A. "Birmingham Jail"
   B. "Wabash Cannonball"
   C. "My Darling Clementine"
❤ ❤ 5. What is Ricky's fine?

113. "Ethel's Home Town"

1. What was Ethel's maiden name?

♥ 2. Who is her former boyfriend?
   A. Chuck Stewart
   B. Larry Sloan
   C. Billy Hackett

3. What does he do for a living in Albuquerque?

4. In honor of Ethel's homecoming, what is the wording on the town's Little Theatre marquee?

♥♥ 5. Name the two songs Ethel performs at the benefit show.

114. "L.A. at Last"

❤ 1. Where do the Ricardos and Mertzes check in when they arrive in Hollywood?

2. Where do Lucy and the Mertzes have lunch?

3. For whom is there a phone call at the bistro, causing Fred to leap out of his seat?
   A. Ava Gardner
   B. Lana Turner
   C. Rita Hayworth

4. For whom does Lucy disguise herself with a long putty nose?

❤❤ 5. Name the executive Ricky meets at MGM.

115. "Don Juan and the Starlets"

♥ 1. Who is sent by the studio to take photos of Ricky and the starlets?
   A. Dore Schary
   B. Charlie Rose
   C. Ross Elliott

2. Complete this line: *"Don Juan* is all about love; it has nothing to do with _____."

3. Where does Ricky go that evening?

4. Why does Lucy assume he has not been home all night?

♥♥ 5. In this episode, Lucy reveals how she actually met Ricky. What were the circumstances?

96

116. "Lucy Gets in Pictures"

1. Where does Lucy go to get "discovered"?

2. Cast in an MGM film, Lucy works with what director?
   A. Sam Jones
   B. Frank Williams
   C. Jack Smith

3. What unique method does Lucy employ to get her name on the screen?

4. What famous song is used as the accompaniment to Lucy's showgirl scene?

5. Who is the Mertzes' old vaudeville friend, now a producer?

♥

117. "The Fashion Show"

---

1. Name the famous dress designer Lucy yearns to meet.
2. After allowing Lucy to purchase a designer original, what dollar limit does Ricky place on her?
   A. $100
   B. $250
   C. $500
♥ 3. What style of outfit does Lucy wear at the fashion show while sporting a California suntan?
4. The charity fashion show is produced for the benefit of
   _____.
♥♥ 5. Who is the salon saleswoman?

118. "The Hedda Hopper Story"

1. Where does Lucy's mother, Mrs. MacGillicuddy, meet Hedda Hopper?
   A. Aboard a plane
   B. In the hotel lobby
   C. In an elevator

2. What scheme does Ricky's new press agent dream up to land Ricky in Hedda's column?

3. Who repeatedly prevents the outcome of the hotel poolside stunt?

♥ 4. What does Mrs. MacGillicuddy answer when asked, "Mother dear, why didn't you tell us it was Hedda Hopper?"

♥♥ 5. Who is Ricky's new public relations representative?

119. "Don Juan Is Shelved"

- 1. Where do Lucy and the Mertzes read the item announcing the cancellation of Ricky's film?
  - A. *Variety*
  - B. *The Hollywood Reporter*
  - C. *The Los Angeles Times*
- 2. Whom does Lucy unwittingly hire to portray fictitious film producer George Spelvin?
- 3. What is MGM's final decision about Ricky's film career?
- 4. True or False: The fan letters of Lucy, Fred, Ethel and Mrs. MacGillicuddy were never mailed.
- 5. How many fan letters are written to try to change MGM's mind about Ricky?

120. "Bull Fight Dance"

❤ 1. For what popular fan magazine has Lucy been asked to write an article?

2. What is the general subject matter of the piece?

3. For what charity is Ricky wanted as host of their TV special?
A. The Heart Fund
B. The Red Cross
C. Boy's Town

4. How does Lucy transform the bull outfit she wears?

❤❤ 5. Name the two songs Ricky attempts to teach Lucy so they can sing them in counterpoint.

❤

121. "Hollywood Anniversary"

1. How does Ricky "remember" the forgotten date of his and Lucy's wedding?
2. Where does Ricky claim a big party has been planned?
   A. The Mocambo
   B. Moulin Rouge
   C. Ciro's
3. True or False: Lucy's date to the Hollywood nightspot is Bobby, the bellboy.
4. What song does Ricky sing on the occasion?

❤❤ 5. How many years have Lucy and Ricky been married?

122. "The Star Upstairs"

♥ 1. How does Lucy first gain entrance to Cornel Wilde's hotel suite?
   A. She dresses like a maid
   B. She impersonates Bobby, the bellboy
   C. She hides under a room service cart

2. How does she get locked outside on the star's balcony?

3. How does Ethel stall Ricky after he asks her of Lucy's whereabouts?

4. True or False: A palm tree breaks Lucy's sudden fall.

♥♥ 5. Counting Wilde, how many movie stars has Lucy spied in Hollywood?

123. "In Palm Springs"

1. Match the annoying habits with the guilty parties.
   A. Lucy   1. Jingling loose change
   B. Ricky   2. Stirring coffee in a cup
   C. Fred   3. Tapping fingers on table
   D. Ethel   4. Eating noisily

2. Separated from Ricky, how does lonely Lucy get her husband to drive to Palm Springs?

♥ 3. The fictitious script girl Rock Hudson talks about is named Adele _____.

4. What is unusual about Lucy's sun-tanning methods?

♥♥ 5. What baseball team are the boys looking forward to seeing play?

123

1. In this episode, what physical problem plagues visiting friend Caroline Appleby?
   A. Sprained ankle
   B. Nearsightedness
   C. Broken arm
♥ 2. Where do Ricky and Fred first encounter Harpo?
3. How does Lucy disguise herself as various movie stars?
4. What musical number does Harpo render on his harp?
♥♥ 5. Where is Caroline, who has stopped over to visit the Ricardos and Mertzes, actually headed?

♥ 124

125. "The Dancing Star"

1. Where does Lucy feign her flirting with Van Johnson?
   A. In the hotel lobby
   B. At MGM
   C. By the hotel pool
2. Johnson is appearing at a nightclub located _____.
♥ 3. To talk Johnson into letting her appear with him, what outlandish promise does Lucy make?
4. What happens to Lucy the night of her performance?
♥♥ 5. Who is Johnson's regular dancing partner?

125

126. "Ricky Needs an Agent"

1. Who is "vice president in charge of Ricky Ricardo"?
   A. Walter Reilly
   B. Dore Schary
   C. Ross Elliott
♥ 2. What familiar name does Lucy use when she poses as Ricky's pushy agent?

3. True or False: Lucy uses a "squeeze play" tactic when talking to the MGM executive.

4. Can you add the missing words to these fictional movie titles: *Gone With the* _____, *It Happened One* _____, *Andy Hardy Meets a* _____, *Meet Me in* _____, *and* _____*Son of Flicka?*

♥♥ 5. Who is the MGM vice president's secretary?

127. "The Tour"

1. Name the sightseeing bus tour on which Lucy and Ethel embark.
   A. Tinsel Town Bus Tour
   B. Hollywood Bus Tour
   C. Grayline Bus Tour

2. Whose house does the tour director describe as having a dollhouse in the backyard?

3. When Lucy informs her fellow bus passengers that Ricky is having lunch with Richard Widmark, the sarcastic bus driver says, "I'll be sure to tell _____ about that at dinner."

♥ 4. What does Lucy want to steal from Widmark's yard?

♥♥ 5. What is the name of Widmark's dog?

♥ 127

1. From which Hollywood restaurant did Lucy secure souvenir chopsticks?
   A. Grauman's Chinese
   B. Don the Beachcomber
   C. China Princess

2. According to Fred, which famous movie horse possesses a smaller foot than Ethel's?

❤ 3. When Fred spies Lucy and Ethel in the midst of their footprint-stealing escapade, he claims they are "real Bellevue _____."

4. Ricky discovers that Lucy is wearing a _____ full of cement in the Mertzes' hotel room.

❤❤ 5. What Clark Gable-Jane Russell film is playing at the famed theater?

129. "Lucy and John Wayne"

1. How are Ethel and Lucy described in a newspaper item recounting the theft of John Wayne's footprints from Grauman's Chinese Theatre? "A _____ blonde and a _____ redhead."

2. What John Wayne film is about to premiere at the theatre?

♥ 3. How does Fred spell John Wayne's last name when he tries to "forge" the Duke's signature on a cement slab?

4. Who is Wayne's masseur?
   A. Harry
   B. George
   C. Butch

♥♥ 5. Who is Lucy and Ethel's hotel beautician?

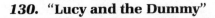

130. "Lucy and the Dummy"

1. What would Ricky rather do than perform at a big studio party?
   A. Go fishing
   B. Go to a ballgame
   C. Play golf
2. How does Lucy manage to involve Ricky in the show without his actual presence?
3. The song to which Lucy dances is titled "I Get _____."
4. As a result of her hilarious performance at the studio party, what happens to Lucy?
❤❤ 5. Name the MGM executive who solicits Ricky's involvement.

131. "Ricky Sells the Car"

1. After selling the Pontiac, what mistake does Ricky make regarding the trip home to New York?
2. What make of motorcycle do the Mertzes buy?
3. What mode of train travel is intended for the Mertzes?
   A. Compartments
   B. Upper berths
   C. Lower berths
4. The group travels on a Union Pacific _____.
❤❤ 5. To whom does Ricky sell the convertible?

132. "The Great Train Robbery"

1. Where has Lucy absentmindedly left her purse containing the train tickets?
2. What is the train's first stop?
   A. Pasadena
   B. Bakersfield
   C. Barstow
3. True or False: The occupant of the train compartment adjacent to the Ricardos' is a jewel thief.
❤ 4. What repeated chaos does Lucy create aboard the train?
❤❤ 5. What food does Lucy order for her mother?

133. "Homecoming"

1. What movie star tale does Lucy have considerable trouble relating to her friends and neighbors?
2. To what legendary screen idol does Mrs. Trumbull liken Ricky?
3. Name the newspaper reporter who interviews Lucy.
   A. Nancy Graham
   B. Eleanor Harris
   C. Calvin Peabody
4. Complete this Lucy line: "And if you want another roast pig, you can crawl in the oven yourself, _____!"
❤❤ 5. What year does Lucy say she graduated from high school?

134. "The Ricardos Are Interviewed"

1. The TV program on which Lucy and Ricky appear is called _____ to _____.
2. Who is Johnny Clark?
   A. A TV producer
   B. Ricky's agent
   C. A press agent
3. True or False: The Ricardos and Mertzes have an argument over whether they can appear on the TV show too.
4. What does Lucy do on the air that prevents her from talking coherently?
❤❤ 5. Who is the host of the interview show?

1. What confusion prevents Ricky from appearing in Fred's lodge show?
2. Who is Fred's "countrified" friend? "Rattlesnake"_____.
3. What song does Lucy yodel?
   A. "Home on the Range"
   B. "Birmingham Jail"
   C. "Back in the Saddle"
💗 4. Name the bell-chiming act at the rodeo.
💗💗 5. What significance does the *Pleasant Peasant* operetta have?

135

114

136. "Nursery School"

1. In what best-selling book does Lucy read that nursery school might not be the proper place for Little Ricky?
❤ 2. Reluctant to enroll the child, Lucy tries to "hide" Little Ricky. How does she accomplish this feat?
3. What medical problem suddenly besets the youngster?
4. What does Lucy sneak into Little Ricky's hospital room to make him feel more at home?
❤❤ 5. Who is the boy's pediatrician?

1. Ethel says she doesn't want to go to Europe because "it's so
   _____!"

♥ 2. How much money does Ricky claim it will take to pay for Lucy
   and Ethel's expenses?
   A. $2,000
   B. $3,000
   C. $4,000

3. In order to raise enough money to go to Europe, Lucy and
   Ethel hold a raffle at a local appliance shop. What is raffled off?

4. What finally changes Ricky's mind about bringing Lucy and
   Ethel along?

♥ ♥ 5. Who runs the appliance store?

138. "The Passports"

1. How many affidavits does Lucy need to prove her birth?
❤ 2. What prompts Lucy to remember hometown chum Helen Erickson's married name?
3. True or False: Helen's husband Sidney is an attorney.
4. Who is the MacGillicuddy family doctor?
   A. Dr. Simpson
   B. Dr. Munsen
   C. Dr. Peterson
❤❤ 5. Name the song Lucy and the doctor sang together years ago.

138

1. How does Lucy intend to cure Fred's seasickness?
2. What time does the Passport Office close?
3. After taking too many seasickness pills, Lucy and Fred _____ on the ferry.
♥ 4. How many trips to Staten Island does the pair take?
    A. Four
    B. Five
    C. Six
♥♥ 5. At the Passport Office, why does Lucy attempt to slug Ricky?

♥ 139

140. "Bon Voyage"

1. Why does Lucy disembark from the ship before it sails for Europe?
   A. She left her purse containing the tickets with her mother
   B. She wanted to kiss Little Ricky again
   C. She wanted to buy a magazine
❤ 2. What prevents Lucy from returning to the ship before it leaves the dock?
3. Lucy first attempts to join Ricky and the Mertzes on the *Constitution* by boarding _____.
4. From her lofty position in a helicopter, what does Lucy say the ship looks like?
❤❤ 5. Where does Lucy catch the whirlybird?

141. "Second Honeymoon"

1. For how many years have the Mertzes been married?
   A. 18
   B. 25
   C. 30

2. What tournament does Lucy sign up for?

❤ 3. Complete this Lucy line: "With everyone paired off, I'm surprised the ship isn't called the S.S. _____."

4. Lucy teams up with Kenneth _____ for the sporting event.

❤❤ 5. Where does Ricky's band play aboard the ship?

141

142. "Lucy Meets the Queen"

❤ 1. Name the three book titles Lucy jokingly tells the Buckingham Palace guard.

2. Where is Ricky appearing in London?
   A. The Palladium
   B. The Hippodrome
   C. Buckingham Palace

3. How does Lucy develop a cramp in her leg?

4. What is the theme of Ricky's show?

❤❤ 5. Shortly after she arrives in London, Lucy exclaims, "No wonder the [British] left here to go to America." To what is she referring?

143. "The Fox Hunt"

1. What is British film producer Sir Clive's last name?
   A. Richardson
   B. Fredrickson
   C. Wilkinson
2. What is his beautiful daughter, Angela Randall's, aspiration?
❤ 3. At the fox hunt, Lucy's mount is "_____ Boy."
4. Who wins the hunt, and how?
❤❤ 5. Where is the hunt held?

144. "Lucy Goes to Scotland"

1. Name the MacGillicuddy home in Scotland.
   A. Kilmartin
   B. Kildoonan
   C. Kilcuddy
2. Why are the townspeople so happy to see Lucy?
3. How often does the two-headed dragon eat?
   A. Every 10 years
   B. Every year
   C. Every 30 years
4. Complete this song title: "I'm in Love with _____."
5. In this dream sequence episode, what is Ricky's name?

145. "Paris at Last"

1. How many dollars' worth of francs does Lucy buy from the street "banker"?
   A. $10
   B. $20
   C. $50

❤ 2. How many francs does Lucy pay for the sidewalk artist's masterpiece?

3. What causes the sidewalk cafe chef to become outraged at snail-eating Lucy?

4. Which language is not employed to extricate Lucy from her legal dilemma—Spanish, French, Italian, or German?

❤❤ 5. Where is the foursome staying in Paris?

1. Where do the Ricardos and Mertzes encounter Charles Boyer?

2. Who urges Lucy to powder her nose before she attempts to meet the famed Frenchman?
   A. Ethel
   B. Fred
   C. Ricky

♥ 3. What fictitious name does Boyer use when he meets Lucy and Ethel? Maurice _____.

4. What is Lucy doing when "Boyer" is kissing her on the arm?

♥♥ 5. In whose newspaper column does Lucy read that Ricky is to meet with Boyer about a possible TV-acting assignment?

♥ —————————————————— 146

147. "Lucy Gets a Paris Gown"

1. The avant garde dress designer is Jacques _____.
2. How does Lucy go about pursuading Ricky to buy her an expensive French gown?
   - A. Non-stop nagging
   - B. Staged hunger strike
   - C. Cancels all of Ricky's appointments
3. In response to what situation does Lucy say, "It's a 3-D picture of a roast chicken"?
4. From what are the original hats, provided by Ricky and Fred, made?
♥♥ 5. How much do two designer gowns cost?

148. "Lucy in the Swiss Alps"

1. When Ricky is separated from his orchestra, what song does a Bavarian band attempt to play as an audition?
2. To take Ricky's mind off the missing musicians, Lucy suggests an afternoon of mountain climbing. What causes the so-called avalanche?
3. Who has leftover food?
   - A. Lucy
   - B. Ricky
   - C. Fred
4. When Ethel reveals, during a "truth-telling" session, that she was 19 when she married Fred, what does Mr. Mertz remark? "You were _____!"
♥♥ 5. Where does Fred send Ricky's orchestra instead of to Lucerne?

149. "Lucy Gets Homesick"

1. Where in Italy does Lucy get homesick?
   A. Naples
   B. Florence
   C. Genoa

2. Name the shoeshine boy befriended by Lucy in the hotel lobby.

3. What makes the repeated trips to the hotel telephone so difficult?

4. True or False: Of all the Italian children at the *in absentia* birthday party, only Little Maria really has a birthday.

❤❤ 5. What is the room number of the Ricardos' bridal suite?

150. "Lucy's Italian Movie"

❤ 1. What famous Italian movie producer does Lucy meet aboard a train?

2. The film he is about to produce is titled _____ *Grapes*.

3. What do the vineyard locals liken Lucy's feet to?
   A. Mussolini's
   B. Pizza pies
   C. Meatballs

4. True or False: Lucy gets into a fight in the wine vat because she has decided to rest from her grape-stomping chores.

❤❤ 5. Where exactly does Lucy "soak up some local color"?

151. "Lucy's Bicycle Trip"

1. Where are the Ricardos and Mertzes headed?

2. What item does a farmer *not* provide for the foursome's breakfast—milk, bread, cheese or jam?

❤ 3. Why does Lucy encounter problems at the Italian-French border?

4. At what hotel does Lucy try to contact Ricky with the plea, "Help"?
   A. Plaza Hotel
   B. Casino Inn
   C. Hotel Royale

❤❤ 5. What number does Lucy plaster on herself for the so-called bicycle race?

152. "Lucy Goes to Monte Carlo"

1. Despite Ricky's protestations, where do Lucy and Ethel have dinner?
2. Where does Lucy find the gambling chip that gets her into so much hot water?
   A. Under her dinner plate
   B. On the casino floor
   C. In her purse
3. Where does Lucy hide the 875,000 francs she has "won"?
4. True or False: Ricky finds the monetary windfall in Lucy's bureau drawer.
❤❤ 5. From whom does Lucy later claim Ethel has inherited the money?

---

153. "Return Home from Europe"

---

1. What airline is chosen for the trip home?
   A. Pan American
   B. Trans World Airlines
   C. Global Airways
2. Who is Mrs. Bigsbee, and what is her first name?
3. What does Lucy name her new "child," the disguised cheese?
♥ 4. True or False: After Lucy and Ethel eat all the cheese they can, Lucy hides the leftover portions so she won't be assessed extra baggage charges.
♥♥ 5. What is the luggage weight limit that makes Lucy's plans to bring home the cheese a problem?

♥————————————————————————————153

154. "Lucy and Bob Hope"

1. Specifically, why does Lucy want to meet Bob Hope?
♥ 2. How is Bob rendered unconscious at the baseball game?
3. What disguise does Lucy employ to gain contact with the comedian after the hotdog vendor scheme fails?
4. The song the Ricardos and Hope sing at Ricky's new Club Babalu is "Nobody Loves _____."
♥♥ 5. At what baseball game does Lucy encounter Hope?

155. "Lucy Meets Orson Welles"

1. Why is Orson Welles at Macy's department store?
   A. Autographing copies of his book
   B. Autographing copies of his record album
   C. Shopping for clothes
2. What Shakespearean play did Lucy say she once appeared in at Jamestown High School?
3. Lucy's high school dramatics coach was Miss _____.
❤ 4. What part does Lucy play in Welles's act at Ricky's club?
❤❤ 5. Why does Lucy go to Macy's?

---

156. "Little Ricky Gets Stage Fright"

1. True or False: Little Ricky's case of stage fright is set off when the music school discusses nervousness.
2. Who operates the child's music school?
   A. Miss Hopkins
   B. Mr. Crawford
   C. Mr. Crandall
3. Who asks excitedly, "Little Ricky fell off a horse?"
4. Ethel employs _____ psychology to talk Little Ricky into performing.
❤❤ 5. What member of the kiddie band contracts the measles?

---

157. "Little Ricky Learns to Play the Drums"

1. How does Lucy try to influence Little Ricky's future career plans?
❤ 2. Where does Ricky buy Little Ricky's snare drum?
   A. Schirmer's Music
   B. Sam Goody
   C. Henry Adler Music
3. The Ricardos have an apartment lease that encompasses _____ years.
4. True or False: When Little Ricky's incessant drumming becomes more than the Mertzes can bear, Fred attempts to hasten the Ricardos' departure by shutting off their water.
❤❤ 5. What is the impromptu title of Lucy's loud mambo?

158. "Visitor from Italy"

♥ 1. Where in Italy did the Ricardos and Mertzes meet Mario Orsatti?

2. True or False: Mario has come to New York City to study opera.

3. What subsistence job does Ricky offer Mario at the Club Babalu?
   A. Waiter
   B. Busboy
   C. Cook

4. What prevents Mario from working at the pizza parlor?

♥♥ 5. How much money does Mario arrive in New York with?

159. "Off to Florida"

1. Why do Lucy and Ethel resort to sharing a ride with a stranger?
2. What type of sandwiches does Mrs. Grundy offer Lucy and Ethel, prompting Lucy to say they taste like "buttered grass"?
♥ 3. Where does Grundy's car experience a flat tire?
   A. South Carolina
   B. North Carolina
   C. Virginia
4. True or False: Lucy and Ethel eventually arrive in Florida by hitching a ride on a grapefruit truck.
♥♥ 5. Name the infamous hatchet murderess.

---

160. "Deep Sea Fishing"

1. At what Miami Beach hotel are the Ricardos and Mertzes staying?
   A. Fountainebleau
   B. Eden Roc
   C. Miami Hilton
2. Why is the figure of $150 decided upon as the "who-will-catch-the-largest-fish contest" wager?
❤ 3. What type of fish does each "team" purchase at a market?
4. True or False: Lucy or Ethel caught a fish.
❤❤ 5. What is the Ricardos' hotel room number?

161. "Desert Island"

1. True or False: Lucy schemes to keep Ricky from judging a beauty contest in Miami.
2. How does she plan to have the boat run out of gas in the middle of the ocean?
3. What part does a Thermos jug play?
💜 4. What is happening on the "desert island"?
💜💜 5. Name the actor encountered on the island.

162. "The Ricardos Visit Cuba"

1. True or False: The head of the Ricardo clan in Cuba is Uncle Marco.

2. Without realizing what she is saying in Spanish, what does Lucy call the relative?
   A. "A big horse"
   B. "A fat pig"
   C. "A mean donkey"

♥ 3. The brand of cigars Lucy attempts to purchase as a gift for the elder Ricardo is called Corona _____.

4. What song do Ricky and Little Ricky perform in tandem?

♥♥ 5. Where are Ricky and Little Ricky appearing?

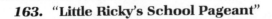

163. "Little Ricky's School Pageant"

1. What role does Ricky play in the school production?
2. Who is Little Ricky's co-star?
   A. Amy
   B. Susie
   C. Margaret
♥ 3. Why does Ethel get the part of the fairy godmother?
4. The title of the show is *The* _____ *Forest.*
♥♥ 5. Who is the producer of the pageant?

164. "Lucy and the Loving Cup"

1. For which famous jockey is the loving cup Lucy gets stuck on her head intended?

❤ 2. True or False: Lucy gets it stuck on her head because she claims it would make a nice hat.

3. What subway line do Lucy and Ethel use to get to a silversmith who promises to free Lucy from the trophy?
   A. IRT
   B. BMT
   C. IND

4. Under what circumstances is the loving cup finally presented to the guest of honor?

❤❤ 5. After losing Ethel on the subway, at what station does Lucy eventually disembark from the train?

♥

165. "Little Ricky Gets a Dog"

1. Which one of these pets does Little Ricky *not* own?
   A. Frogs
   B. Goldfish
   C. Hamster
♥ 2. What major obstacle stands in the way of his keeping the new puppy?
3. What does Little Ricky name the dog?
4. Complete this Fred Mertz line: "I'd rather live with a little dog than a _____."
♥♥ 5. Who gives the puppy to Little Ricky?

166. "Lucy and Superman"

1. Why do Lucy and Caroline Appleby get into an argument?

2. Complete this Lucy line: "If I don't produce Superman, my name will be _____."

3. True or False: Lucy snags George Reeves for the party because Charlie Appleby is a friend of his agent.

♥ 4. How does Lucy get locked out on the ledge of the apartment building?

♥♥ 5. According to a comment in this episode, how many years have Lucy and Ricky been married?

167. "Lucy Wants to Move to the Country"

1. True or False: Lucy tries to convince Ricky that the family should move to the country because city life is not good for her health.
2. How much deposit does Ricky put down on the new home?
   A. $500
   B. $1,000
   C. $2,500
3. Where is the house located?
❤ 4. If Fred's nickname in Lucy's scheme to get back the house deposit is "Fingers," what is Ricky's?
❤❤ 5. Name the present owners of the house.

143

---

168. "Lucy Hates to Leave"

1. Lucy claims that Ricky is suffering from "a bad case of homeowner's _____."

❤ 2. Initially, how long do the Ricardos intend to live with the Mertzes before their move to the country?
   A. Two days
   B. Four days
   C. One week

3. What do the young couple who have rented the Ricardo apartment intend to do with Lucy's coffee table?

4. What ultimately prevents the Ricardos from moving on schedule?

❤❤ 5. Name the couple who have rented Apartment 3-D.

♥

169. "Lucy Misses the Mertzes"

♥ 1. True or False: Aside from kisses and good-byes, the Ricardos and Mertzes exchange keys before their tearful separation.

2. What edible housewarming gift is delivered to the new Ricardo residence from the Mertzes?

3. Who is Little Ricky's new friend?
   A. Billy
   B. Peter
   C. Tommy

4. What makes it impossible for the Ricardos and Mertzes to coordinate their "travel" plans?

♥♥ 5. How much does Fred spend on train fare to the country?

170. "Lucy Gets Chummy with the Neighbors"

1. How much money does Ricky say Lucy can spend on furniture for the new house?
   A. $500
   B. $750
   C. $1,000

❤ 2. How much of a discount does Betty Ramsey, the Ricardos' new neighbor, claim she can get Lucy on new furnishings?

3. Embarrassed to reveal that they can't afford a complete household of new furnishings, what style of furniture does Lucy claim she wants instead of Early American?

4. Ralph Ramsey, Betty's husband, works at a New York _____.

❤❤ 5. How much money does Lucy spend?

171. "Lucy Raises Chickens"

1. Through Betty Ramsey's intervention, what magazine wants to photograph the Ricardo home for a layout?
   A. *House Beautiful*
   B. *Interiors*
   C. *House & Garden*
2. Who suggests the chicken-raising scheme as a means of earning extra money?
3. What *finally* convinced the Mertzes to move to the country to help raise the chickens?
❤ 4. How do the baby chicks escape from the den?
❤❤ 5. How many chicks do Lucy and Ethel purchase?

172. "Lucy Does the Tango"

1. How many laying hens do the Ricardos trade for the baby chicks?
   A. 50
   B. 100
   C. 200

❤ 2. How many eggs do Lucy and Ethel purchase to fool their husbands into believing the hens are actually laying a "bumper crop"?

3. Why do Lucy and Ricky suddenly rehearse the tango?

4. True or False: Little Ricky scatters the chickens all over the neighborhood when he suspects his parents want to get out of the egg business.

❤❤ 5. How many eggs have the hens laid after two weeks?

173. "Ragtime Band"

1. Why is Ricky expected to perform?
2. What instrument does Fred profess to play?
3. What is Lucy's lone tune—"Sweet Sue" or "Glow Worm"?
❤ 4. The calypso song Lucy, Ricky, Fred, Ethel, and Little Ricky eventually perform is titled "The Woman _____."
❤❤ 5. What one song does Ethel claim to know on the piano?

174. "Lucy's Night in Town"

1. What musical do the Ricardos and Mertzes intend to see on Broadway?
   A. *Guys and Dolls*
   B. *The Most Happy Fella*
   C. *My Fair Lady*
♥ 2. What exactly is the theater ticket mix-up that Lucy perpetrates?
3. Why is Fred carrying $500 in cash on him?
4. Why does the foursome share only two theater seats?
♥♥ 5. In an effort to waste time to cover her mistake, how many times does Lucy claim she must chew each mouthful of food?

150

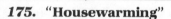

175. "Housewarming"

💗 1. What touches off the "bosom buddy" friendship between Ethel Mertz and Betty Ramsey?

2. True or False: Lucy overhears a conversation Ethel is having with Betty because of the telephone party line.

3. What do the Mertzes give to the Ricardos as a housewarming gift?
   A. A basket of fruit
   B. A candy dish
   C. A candlestick

4. Complete this Lucy line: "Ever since they had lunch here, they've been as _____."

💗💗 5. Name the three married couples Lucy invites to her dinner party.

176. "Building a Bar-B-Q"

1. What prompts Lucy to ask Ricky, "Why don't you call up Little Freddie Mertz and ask him to come over and play?"
2. What touches off the wedding ring argument Lucy and Ricky have?
   A. Lucy takes it off to wash dishes and leaves it on a window ledge
   B. Lucy loses it in the hen house
   C. Lucy wants a new one
♥ 3. How do Lucy and Ethel con Ricky and Fred into building the barbecue?
4. How does the ring eventually wind up in the hamburger?
♥♥ 5. What prompts Lucy to say, "My wedding ring is someplace over the Long Island Sound"?

177. "Country Club Dance"

1. To whom is siren Diana related?
   A. The Munsens
   B. The Baileys
   C. The Ramseys
2. Who dances the most with Diana at the country club—Ricky, Fred, or Ralph Ramsey?
♥ 3. What womanly "tricks" do the jealous wives think up to "woo" back their husbands?
4. True or False: Diana's true love is Elvis Presley.
♥♥ 5. What is Diana's last name?

💗

178. "Lucy Raises Tulips"

💗 1. What prize would Lucy like to win at the Westport Garden Show?

2. Who has won the coveted title three years in a row?

3. Why has Ricky neglected to finish mowing their lawn?

4. Who mowed down Lucy's tulips?
   - A. Fred
   - B. Ricky
   - C. Ethel

💗💗 5. Where does Lucy purchase the wax tulips?

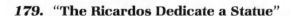

179. "The Ricardos Dedicate a Statue"

1. Name the civic event that has all of Westport involved.
   A. American Revolution Day
   B. Westport Founders' Day
   C. Yankee Doodle Day
2. What is Fred's role in the ceremonies?
❤ 3. Why does Lucy hastily jump into the station wagon and drive off, breaking the statue?
4. _____ gives the dedication speech at the event.
❤❤ 5. Who has sculpted the unique statue?

180. Cast of Characters

Match the *I Love Lucy* character with his or her description.

1. Alvin Littlefield
2. Mario Orsatti
3. Percy Livermore
4. Dan Jenkins
5. Ben Benjamin
6. Mr. Meriweather
7. Mr. Ritter
8. Mr. O'Brien
9. Zeb Allen
10. Dickie Davis

A. Venetian gondelier
B. Grocery man
C. Owner of Tropicana
D. TV show host
E. Talent scout
F. Used clothing dealer
G. English tutor
H. Used furniture dealer
I. Broadway producer
J. Neighbor

Lucy and Ricky with Mr. Meriweather.

181. Whodunit

Who...

1. ...arranges the interview with magazine writer Eleanor Harris?
2. ...is the district attorney's representative threatening to arrest Lucy for fraud when she stages a raffle without the proper credentials?
3. ...play Lucy's "farewell dirge"?
4. ...asks Lucy to go to Knott's Berry Farm?
5. ...is responsible for perpetrating the "handcuff" incident?

182. Fill in the Blanks

1. Renita's Cuban dance partner is named _____.
2. Lucy's "fake illness" came into the country on "the hind legs of the _____ bird."
3. Lucy and Ethel attempt to sell their surplus beef for _____¢ a pound.
4. In the Wednesday Afternoon Fine Arts League operetta, Fred is the proprietor of the Inn on the River _____.
5. The Mertzes once toiled in a diner in the city of _____.

Ethel and Fred.

183. Mixed-Up Lucy

You will find the answers to the clues provided hidden among
the maze of letters below. To locate them, simply read forward,
backward, up, down, and diagonally. You must always travel in a
straight line, and you cannot skip letters. Draw a circle around
each title that you discover. Letters are permitted to be used
more than once, and words may overlap. You will find that seven
letters remain unused. These will form the last name of a very
important *I Love Lucy* figure when unscrambled.

1. Mrs. Mertz
2. Lucy at The Brown _____
3. Little Ricky's babysitter
4. Lucy and Ricky
5. Vivian _____
6. Mr. Oppenheimer
7. Lucy's network
8. Ricky's homeland
9. Fred and Ethel
10. Carroll, Schiller or Weiskopf
11. *I Love* _____
12. Ricky's hit song
13. Lucille _____
14. "Lucy" player, Ross _____
15. Studios or Productions

L	J	E	S	S	R	O	L
U	L	A	B	A	B	D	E
C	E	U	C	Y	A	R	L
Y	H	A	B	E	L	A	L
Z	T	R	E	M	L	C	I
D	E	S	I	L	U	I	O
D	Y	R	O	B	E	R	T
W	F	V	A	N	C	E	T

184. About Ethel Mertz

1. Where was Ethel born?
2. What does her father do for a living?
3. Where did she have her gallstones removed?
4. Name her butcher uncle and his wife.
5. What is Ethel's middle name?
6. What is her father's name?

185. Role Call

Identify the performer who played each duo of *I Love Lucy* characters.

1. Percy Livermore and Dan Jenkins
2. Cynthia Harcourt and Evelyn Bigsbee
3. Freddie Fillmore and Ben Benjamin
4. Mario Orsatti and Mr. Meriweather
5. Will Potter and Bert Willoughby

Desi with actor Frank Nelson.

186. True or False?

1. Lucy Ricardo graduated from high school.
2. In Hollywood, Lucy meets Jimmy Durante.
3. The Mertzes own the New York City apartment building free and clear.
4. Ricky is an only child.
5. Little Ricky was almost named Romeo.
6. Fred Mertz has no interest in sports.
7. Lucy "learned" to play the saxophone because she once was in love with a football player.
8. Mrs. Trumbull has no known relatives.
9. The Ricardos and Mertzes visited Germany.
10. Ricky is replaced briefly as the star of the Tropicana.

1. Can you sing the lyrics to the first eight bars of the *I Love Lucy* theme song?
2. What day of the week does the Wednesday Afternoon Fine Arts League meet?
3. What is Lucy's middle name?
4. What does Fred name *his* half of the diner?
5. How much money do the Ricardos charge when they sublease their apartment?
6. What does Fred pay for the motorcycle he intends to drive from California to New York?
7. Name the "unusual" food Lucy orders at the sidewalk café in Paris.
8. For whom does Lucy buy an enormous piece of cheese in Europe?
9. To what does Lucy liken Mrs. Grundy's sandwiches?
10. Name the two women Lucy "portrays" to help sell her salad dressing.

♥

The Wednesday Afternoon Fine Arts League elects officers in Lucy's apartment.

188. Wives Match

Match the man with his better half.

1. Bill Foster
2. Alvin Littlefield
3. Charlie Appleby
4. Bill Hall
5. Sam Johnson

A. Caroline
B. Grace
C. Nancy
D. Phoebe
E. Lou Ann

♥

189. Which One Doesn't Belong?

From each group, select one entry which should not be included and explain why.

1. Gittelman / Rabwin / Parker / Molin / Robinson
2. Moore / Benson / O'Brien / Lewis / Stewart
3. Grace Munsen / Judith Applegate / Hazel Pierce / Ethel Mertz / Ruth Knickerbocker
4. Cary Grant / Robert Taylor / Lana Turner / Van Johnson / Richard Widmark
5. Ava Gardner / Rita Hayworth / Jane Russell / Arlene Dahl / Betty Grable

♥

190. Staffers

Match the behind-the-scenes personnel with his/her function.

1. Hal King
2. Madelyn Pugh
3. Karl Freund
4. Jess Oppenheimer
5. Eliot Daniel
6. Elois Jenssen
7. James Kern
8. Della Fox
9. Dann Cahn
10. Wilbur Hatch

A. Makeup artist
B. Costume designer
C. Writer
D. Musical conductor
E. Director
F. Film editor
G. Cinematographer
H. Producer
I. Costumer
J. Musical arranger

Lucy and Desi with Jess Oppenheimer.

191. Numbers Game

1. What is the exact address of the Mertz apartment building in New York City?
2. How much does it cost to transport the huge walk-in meat freezer to the apartment building?
3. What is the alcoholic content of Vitameatavegamin?
4. What royalty fee is saved when Lucy writes her own operetta?
5. When forced to tell the truth, how much does Lucy say she weighs?

192. Can You Recall?

1. What is Fred's middle name?
2. How many jars of salad dressing are sold?
3. Name the employment agency Lucy and Ethel once engaged.
4. What do the Littlefields "serve" at their dinner party for the Ricardos?
5. What is Fred's hometown?

With what character and situation would you associate these famous lines?

1. "I'm just dying to see those lousy movies again!"
2. "On behalf of the tubby trio, I welcome you to our flabby foursome."
3. "I'll be sure to tell Lana about it at dinner."
4. "I think he takes in dirty dishes from other restaurants."
5. "I hope we find a mechanic in there."
6. "I've been waiting ten years for you to lay that egg!"
7. "I didn't tell a soul, and they all promised to keep it a secret."
8. "What a relief. I thought he'd never quit!"
9. "What are you trying to do, lose the case for us?"
10. "Wouldn't you like to see me die?"

Lucy's big break in the movies.

ANSWERS

Quiz 1
1. B
2. Dogs for an act at the club
3. Lucy watches Ricky put some sleeping powder in a glass and assumes it is poison
4. A skillet
5. Marilyn

Quiz 2
1. B
2. True
3. "Guadalajara"
4. At the fights
5. 18

Quiz 3
1. C
2. She gets all dolled up in a tight-fitting, sequined dress
3. Poker
4. Carmen Miranda's
5. Five

Quiz 4
1. B
2. Dog
3. False; the piano player is Marco
4. "Cuban Pete"
5. 12

Quiz 5
1. Freddie Fillmore
2. A
3. True
4. Introduce Ricky to a man whom she claims is her long-lost first husband
5. 25 cents

Quiz 6
1. A
2. "Babalu"
3. Cello

4. Lucy is offered a contract, not Ricky
5. "Buffo"

Quiz 7
1. A
2. "We're all odd, aren't we?"
3. False; Tillie is his deceased cocker spaniel
4. The medium, Madame Ethel Mertzola
5. Taurus

Quiz 8
1. C
2. Lucy
3. Photographer
4. *Look*
5. Maggie

Quiz 9
1. Fort Dix
2. B
3. Knitting
4. They are squirreled away in the hall closet and forgotten
5. Sunday

Quiz 10
1. For an act at the club
2. She sleeps with it on
3. B
4. True
5. $3,500

Quiz 11
1. A
2. *Arroz con pollo* (chicken and rice)
3. False; the lace is black
4. She sneaks into the chorus line at the Tropicana
5. "Jezebel"

Quiz 12
1. A parisian apache dance

2. French hand laundry
3. C
4. In the Ricardo bedroom
5. Five

Quiz 13
1. Middle
2. A
3. She sings the "auf" in each stanza
4. True
5. "Songs and Witty Sayings"

Quiz 14
1. B
2. Jimmy and Timmy
3. $5 per hour
4. "Ragtime Cowboy Joe"
5. The Blue Bird Club

Quiz 15
1. Miss Lewis
2. Mr. Ritter
3. C
4. True
5. Five years

Quiz 16
1. Talullah Bankhead
2. C
3. Gobloots
4. Zorch
5. *Abnormal Psychology*

Quiz 17
1. *A Tree Grows in Havana*
2. False; Fred cannot do a Spanish accent
3. A
4. Lucy's mother
5. Darryl B. Mayer

Quiz 18
1. "Sweet Sue"
2. The Ricardos continue singing long after the Mertzes have departed
3. True
4. B
5. Five more months

Quiz 19
1. A
2. Martha
3. She gets her leg caught in it
4. "Martha"
5. "Dance of the Flowers"

Quiz 20
1. False; it's Peggy Dawson and Arthur Morton
2. Arthur proclaims his love for Lucy
3. They dress up as very old people
4. "He's baba'ed his last lu"
5. 35

Quiz 21
1. That she not set foot in the apartment
2. A
3. They are actors
4. False; she disguises herself as a chair by donning a slipcover
5. Sergeant Morton

Quiz 22
1. The YMCA
2. True
3. Say she got hit by a bus
4. A
5. The Mertzes' awning

Quiz 23
1. For a TV role
2. To get back at Ricky for growing the mustache
3. As a harem girl with a veil
4. No
5. Bulldog Cement #7

Quiz 24
1. Through charades
2. A
3. True
4. Grace Foster and the milkman
5. $5

Quiz 25
1. $50 that the girls can't live like

167

the people in the 1890s
2. Matrons'
3. B
4. Homemade bread
5. Mrs. Pettybone and Mrs. Pomerantz

Quiz 26
1. Ricky Bicardi
2. A
3. "I Love You Truly"
4. Mayor
5. At the Byram River Beagle Club in Greenwich, Connecticut

Quiz 27
1. For a club bazaar
2. C
3. An elephant
4. Pockets
5. Dr. Tom Robinson

Quiz 28
1. Perez
2. B
3. Fred
4. "African Wedding Dance"
5. Carlos and Maria

Quiz 29
1. A
2. True
3. Stump
4. The lock has not yet been removed
5. 69 cents a pound or $483

Quiz 30
1. Candy
2. It contains alcohol
3. Poop out at parties
4. B
5. She dons a Philip Morris "Johnny" outfit and gets inside a hollowed-out TV set and does her act for Ricky

Quiz 31
1. The Maharincess of Franistan

2. C
3. False; she faints when he sings "I Get Ideas"
4. Henna-rinsess
5. The Shah of Persia

Quiz 32
1. Freddie Fillmore
2. The director of the Internal Revenue
3. The sap runs every two years
4. To scrape the barnacles off her hull
5. $500

Quiz 33
1. Phoebe
2. Seven o'clock
3. Seal
4. B
5. Split pea

Quiz 34
1. A
2. So he will realize that, by comparison to a group of bald-headed men, he has no problems
3. A hat and toupee
4. "You have to bake for 20 minutes."
5. $10

Quiz 35
1. C
2. Xavier Valdez, "King of the Konga"
3. Maurice
4. True
5. 75

Quiz 36
1. A
2. Furnace pipe
3. She dons painter's pants and maneuvers down the side of the building on a scaffold
4. A string of pearls
5. Their 11th

Quiz 37
1. The Civil War
2. C
3. False; he lives in Yonkers
4. A straw hat
5. *Guest Stars*

Quiz 38
1. A
2. *Pleasant*
3. Prince Lancelot, Lily of the Valley, and Friar Quinn
4. "I love to sing and dance a lot."
5. She pays for the items with a postdated check because the club treasury is bankrupt

Quiz 39
1. A
2. Ricky will make *arroz con pollo* (chicken and rice) and Fred will bake a seven-layer chocolate cake
3. They cannot keep up with the swift-moving conveyor belt
4. Five-pound boxes of chocolates
5. Acme Employment Agency

Quiz 40
1. False; "Glow Worm"
2. Fred
3. A man's hat and gloves
4. A
5. Celeron High School

Quiz 41
1. B
2. Pool of stagnation
3. On the roof of the apartment building
4. "21"
5. A neighbor who spies the wives on the roof

Quiz 42
1. Their 25th wedding anniversary

2. Ricky
3. She reveals her legs by lifting up her skirt
4. It blows up
5. 20 inches

Quiz 43
1. The Home Show
2. Rodgers and Hammerstein's
3. A
4. She buys paint and wallpaper
5. $75

Quiz 44
1. He writes everything on a small chalk board
2. "Flapper Follies of 1927"
3. Carlsbad Caverns
4. A
5. Mr. Chambers

Quiz 45
1. A
2. Handy Dandy
3. They've reported the death of another salesman
4. False; he buys her a washing machine
5. "There's a Brand New Baby at Our House"

Quiz 46
1. True
2. C
3. The doctor starts making a pass at Lucy and Ricky gets jealous
4. Sing
5. Dr. Henry Molin

Quiz 47
1. She promises her a new cashmere sweater and matching beaded bag if she will nominate her
2. C
3. True
4. Lucy *and* Ethel—it's a tie
5. Lillian

Quiz 48

1. Ricky tosses a book at her and it hits her in the eye
2. A
3. Box
4. False; Fred slugs Ricky
5. Madge and Gordon

Quiz 49

1. B
2. Tables
3. Tom
4. False; it's Harry
5. He is left-handed

Quiz 50

1. Ethel
2. C
3. She travels to the club and slips a note to the maitre d' to give to Ricky
4. "We're Having a Baby"
5. Dauncey

Quiz 51

1. "Okay, unique if it's a boy and euphonious if it's a girl"
2. Waffles
3. Anthony and Cleopatra
4. True
5. "Cheek to Cheek"

Quiz 52

1. "Nothin' Could Be Finer Than to Be in Carolina"
2. C
3. MacGillicuddy
4. "Sweet Adeline"
5. George Watson

Quiz 53

1. Livermore
2. "Tippy Tippy Toe"
3. True
4. He persuades Percy to use *his* brand of "English"
5. "Swell," "okay," and "lousy"

Quiz 54

1. The members of the Wednes-

day Afternoon Fine Arts League
2. Pains in the stomach
3. A "daddy shower"
4. B
5. The sixth

Quiz 55

1. False; it is William Abbott
2. C
3. A bust of her own head
4. $500
5. 50 pounds

Quiz 56

1. A
2. Stanley
3. A voodoo number
4. He faints
5. 45 minutes

Quiz 57

1. B
2. All the money on earth
3. False; "than *South Pacific*"
4. Mrs. Trumbull
5. Six

Quiz 58

1. A
2. That Lucy take complete charge of the baby
3. They turn the Ricardo apartment into a "pig pen" so the maid will get disgusted with all the work
4. False; Ricky does the job
5. Roast beef, a head of lettuce, milk, and jelly

Quiz 59

1. *Indian Tales*
2. Because she is now a mother, interested only in caring for her newborn son
3. A
4. False; Lucy has the baby strapped on her back like a papoose

5. Marilyn

Quiz 60
1. She brings Lucy a small cake, some party hats and wants to celebrate Lucy's birthday with Little Ricky
2. Friends of the Friendless
3. My fellow man
4. C
5. He wants Lucy to bring him some music from home

Quiz 61
1. The Bensons'
2. A
3. True
4. She moves all of Ricky's belongings into unlikely places (like his socks in the desk drawer), then clutters up the living room with sliding ponds and other children's toys and games
5. $20

Quiz 62
1. False; he is a friend of Fred's
2. Lingerie
3. C
4. Caroline Appleby
5. No. 925

Quiz 63
1. B
2. The old furniture
3. In the kitchen
4. Little Orphan Annie
5. The Carrolls

Quiz 64
1. The sports section
2. A
3. She provides the fish and fowl with the help of a car borrowed from the local lodge owner
4. True
5. At Churchill Downs

Quiz 65
1. Left elbow
2. Challenge dance
3. She holds a rose between her teeth, then upstages Ricky with Fred's assistance
4. C
5. Six hours a day for three days

Quiz 66
1. The fights
2. C
3. True
4. Sticky Fingers Sal
5. Sergeant Nelson

Quiz 67
1. B
2. False; he is willing to pay $50
3. On the back porch balcony
4. It breaks through the guard rail and plunges to the ground
5. Joe

Quiz 68
1. Hansen's Dress Shop
2. C
3. Check
4. $50,000
5. Five (to each other)

Quiz 69
1. Ricky Ricardo
2. "Friendship"
3. False; Lucy buys hers at Gimbel's
4. Ham
5. Monday at midnight

Quiz 70
1. A
2. They are forced to wash dishes
3. True
4. Ricky and Fred
5. Xavier

Quiz 71
1. Stevie by four days
2. B

3. Mabel Normand
4. "Acapulco"
5. 13 months

Quiz 72
1. 24
2. Chinese modern
3. C
4. 3-D
5. Professor Falconi

Quiz 73
1. A part in a revue at the Trop-icana
2. First as a lampshade, then be-hind a picture, then inside a bass fiddle case
3. By impersonating a fat, ma-tronly woman
4. A
5. Robert DuBois

Quiz 74
1. A
2. Via a game of charades
3. A painting party
4. An overstuffed chair
5. It is Ethel's turn to host a meeting of the women's club and she's ashamed of her apartment's drab look

Quiz 75
1. B
2. "X"
3. On Ricky's silver cigarette case, then on a drinking glass, and, finally, on a candy dish
4. True
5. A tweed suit

Quiz 76
1. B
2. 1909
3. False; the boxes are from Brooks Brothers
4. As his fashion consultant
5. Zeb Allen

Quiz 77
1. A
2. Arthur "King Cat" Walsh
3. "Varsity Drag"
4. PITT
5. *The Professor and the Coed*

Quiz 78
1. Is Your Spouse a Louse
2. Romero
3. The Five Romero Sisters
4. C
5. The Opal Room

Quiz 79
1. Aunt Martha's Old-Fashioned Salad Dressing
2. Three cents per jar
3. Mary Margaret McMertz
4. B
5. Dickie Davis

Quiz 80
1. B
2. Watching a football game on television
3. He went to bed, upset that his team lost
4. False; Fred does the transfer
5. A Spanish omelet

Quiz 81
1. A
2. Phoebe Emerson's Charm School
3. What's that
4. A tight-fitting leopard-skin dress
5. Lucy—32; Ethel—30

Quiz 82
1. B
2. Stone Marten furs
3. False; she buys him a set of golf clubs
4. In the hall closet
5. Ricky has a meeting with Rod-gers and Hammerstein

Quiz 83
1. Eleanor
2. B
3. He sends out personal invitations to various ladies using Ricky's signature which he forges
4. Minnie Finch
5. 3,000

Quiz 84
1. Nancy
2. C
3. Periwinkle blue
4. Using a tape recorder, she intends to get Sam Johnson to admit his many claims; then she will be able to sue him for fraud
5. Ken

Quiz 85
1. Lucy buys *another* hat
2. A
3. Little pearls
4. Tomato juice
5. $49.50, the price of Lucy's hat

Quiz 86
1. They walk out
2. A western
3. C
4. "Vaya con Dios"
5. "Ricky Ricardo Presents Tropical Rhythms"

Quiz 87
1. A
2. Ricky
3. False; it was in Ricky's pajama top
4. Starch vat
5. Speedy Laundry

Quiz 88
1. Ricky and his band have been booked on a concert tour of the islands
2. *Neighbor*

3. Freddie Fillmore
4. B
5. Water, honey, eggs, a basket, coffee, and pie

Quiz 89
1. B
2. $500
3. *Women from Mars*
4. Atop the Empire State Building
5. Cynthia Harcourt

Quiz 90
1. B
2. *Real*
3. "Ethel Nurtz"
4. *Forever Ember*
5. Dorrance and Company

Quiz 91
1. B
2. Ethel
3. False; she promises that Ricky will lead the band
4. "Twelfth Street Rag"
5. Six

Quiz 92
1. A
2. $2,000
3. A Little Bit of Cuba
4. False; hamburgers get reduced in price
5. Mr. Watson

Quiz 93
1. An Italian cut
2. A
3. At Tony's Italian Restaurant
4. Japanese
5. Mother Carroll, an old vaudeville friend

Quiz 94
1. Xavier
2. Middle boy
3. He sleeps on it without opening it

4. B
5. "Wabash Cannonball"

Quiz 95
1. They buy a bus ticket back to Bent Fork and purposely "lose" it in the apartment house hallway, hoping Ernie will find it
2. Lucy pretends she and Ricky are penniless ... and without food
3. *Chicken Mash*
4. C
5. "Ernie Ford and His Four Hot Chicken Pickers"

Quiz 96
1. Basketball
2. Jimmy Demaret
3. True
4. C
5. Mamie Eisenhower

Quiz 97
1. Maine
2. False; her name is Mrs. Hammond
3. A
4. He was a juror on a murder trial
5. Del Mar, California

Quiz 98
1. A woman's husband ignores her during her time of dire need
2. Baba; lu
3. With Lucy overhearing every word, Ricky mourns Lucy's possible passing
4. B
5. "I'll have to have them altered. They're much too big in the hips."

Quiz 99
1. B

2. He has an early morning recording session
3. False; his name is Milton Frome
4. They marry
5. Carter and Cooke, respectively

Quiz 100
1. A
2. With a charge account opened by the business manager at a local grocery market, Lucy charges all of her neighbors' food orders, pocketing the cash
3. All Pet
4. $1,000
5. $5

Quiz 101
1. *Breakfast with Ricky and Lucy*
2. Slept; mattress
3. A
4. "Phipps is a great big bunch of gyps!"
5. Cromwell, Thatcher and Waterbury

Quiz 102
1. Barney
2. The Mertzes' maid
3. False; he is a cook
4. A
5. "Laugh 'til It Hurts with Mertz and Kurtz"

Quiz 103
1. B
2. True
3. As a matador
4. At Benjamin's hotel room
5. Pete, the grocery delivery boy

Quiz 104
1. B
2. Marilyn Monroe, Ava Gardner, Jane Russell, Yvonne DeCarlo, Arlene Dahl, Betty Grable and Lana Turner

3. "Is it you, Don Juan?"
4. Feed
5. $3 million

Quiz 105
1. A
2. *Pollo*
3. False; he has become a grand-father
4. In the subway
5. Professor Bonanova

Quiz 106
1. Hostess pants
2. B
3. *Teacups*
4. The subject matter of the play suggests the same problem Lucy and Ethel are experiencing and they finally make up as the stage characters do
5. 75 years

Quiz 107
1. Use the telephone
2. Fred
3. B
4. Little bird
5. Two weeks

Quiz 108
1. A
2. Gallstones
3. Cadillac
4. True
5. New Jersey

Quiz 109
1. Pontiac convertible
2. B
3. Lucy
4. She drives the cars down a hill, they unlock bumpers and somehow change positions
5. To call the insurance company about the new car

Quiz 110
1. Mickey
2. Ethel overhears a conversation Lucy and Ricky are having about the Mertzes "tagging along." Ethel's feelings are properly hurt and she and Fred beg off
3. Pitchfork
4. Rail
5. Six o'clock in the morning

Quiz 111
1. Sally
2. A
3. A cheese sandwich
4. True
5. George Skinner

Quiz 112
1. For speeding (going 40 mph in a 15-mph zone)
2. Bent Fork
3. Teensy and Weensy
4. A
5. $50

Quiz 113
1. Potter
2. C
3. He is a reporter for the town's paper, the *Chronicle*
4. "Ethel May Potter—We Never Forgot Her"
5. "My Hero" from *The Chocolate Soldier* and "Shortnin' Bread"

Quiz 114
1. The Beverly Palms Hotel
2. At The Brown Derby
3. A
4. William Holden
5. Bill Sherman

Quiz 115
1. C
2. Marriage
3. To a Hollywood premiere
4. The hotel chambermaid admits to entering the room while Lucy was asleep on the

living room sofa, making up
Ricky's bed and then stealing
out without Lucy's knowledge
5. Marion Strong suggested a
blind date with a Cuban
drummer 15 years before

Quiz 116
1. Schwab's Drugstore
2. B
3. She paints her name on the
soles of her high heels
4. "A Pretty Girl Is Like a Melody"
5. Jimmy O'Connor

Quiz 117
1. Don Loper
2. A
3. A tweed suit
4. Share, Inc.
5. Amzie

Quiz 118
1. A
2. Lucy is to fall in the hotel
swimming pool and Ricky is
to jump in and save her
3. The hotel pool lifeguard
4. "You didn't ask me!"
5. Charlie Pomerantz

Quiz 119
1. A
2. Dore Schary
3. They will pick up his option
and attempt to find a suitable
motion picture property in
which to star him
4. False; they were mailed but no
stamps had been affixed
5. 500

Quiz 120
1. *Photoplay*
2. "What It's Like to Be Married
to Ricky Ricardo"
3. A
4. She changes the face from that
of a ferocious beast to that of

a mincing, false-eyelashed
animal
5. "Humoresque" and "Swannee
River"

Quiz 121
1. He wires the Hall of Records in
Greenwich, Connecticut, re-
questing the exact date
2. A
3. True
4. "Anniversary Waltz"
5. 15

Quiz 122
1. B
2. Wilde decides to nap and
locks the door to his terrace
3. She asks him to sing her a few
songs
4. True
5. 100

Quiz 123
1. A/2, B/3, C/1, D/4
2. She disguises her voice as the
secretary of Dore Schary and
asks Ricky to come to Palm
Springs for an important
meeting
3. Sliff
4. She covers her body from
head to toe, allowing very little
sun to reach her skin
5. The Hollywood Stars

Quiz 124
1. B
2. By the hotel pool
3. She uses various rubber masks
and verbally impersonates the
stars
4. "Take Me Out to the Ballgame"
5. Hawaii

Quiz 125
1. C
2. In the hotel
3. She will name her next child

176

after him; if she doesn't have any more children, she'll change the name of the one she already has
4. At first, she freezes from stage fright, but then relaxes and does a great job
5. Hazel

Quiz 126
1. A
2. Lucille MacGillicuddy
3. True
4. *Cuban Wind, Noche, Conga Player, St. Ricky, Ricky*
5. Miss Klein

Quiz 127
1. C
2. Shirley Temple's
3. Lana
4. A grapefruit
5. "Cap"

Quiz 128
1. B
2. "Trigger"
3. Bait
4. Foot
5. *The Tall Men*

Quiz 129
1. Dishwater; frowsy
2. *Blood Alley*
3. Wain
4. B
5. Irma

Quiz 130
1. A
2. She uses a rubber replica of his head, attaches it to a dummy's body and dances with it
3. Ideas
4. She is offered a studio contract as a comedienne
5. Chip Jackson

Quiz 131
1. He forgets about the Mertzes and buys tickets only for himself and his immediate family
2. Harley-Davidson
3. B
4. Domeliner
5. Ralph Berger

Quiz 132
1. At the Union Station magazine counter
2. A
3. False; he is a jewelry salesman
4. She continually pulls the emergency brake handle, causing the train to make abrupt stops
5. A sandwich

Quiz 133
1. The episode about Richard Widmark's grapefruit
2. Rudolph Valentino
3. A
4. You big ham
5. She never reveals the exact year, but says she graduated "four years after I started"

Quiz 134
1. *Face; Face*
2. B
3. False; their argument has to do with the Ricardos' possible move from the building to a fancy Park Avenue address
4. She bites into a melting chocolate
5. Ed Warren

Quiz 135
1. He thinks he has a radio show to do that night
2. Jones
3. A
4. Lucille Cannonball MacGillicuddy and Her Western Bell-Ringers

5. Lucy and Ethel suggest this show for Fred's lodge happening

Quiz 136
1. *Dr. Spock's Baby Care Book*
2. She sends him off with Fred for the day
3. Tonsillitis
4. His teddy bear
5. Dr. Gittelman

Quiz 137
1. Old
2. B
3. A television set
4. The steamship company will provide free passage for Ricky and his band if they entertain aboard the ship
5. Mr. Feldman

Quiz 138
1. Two
2. Ethel mentions something about the Kaiser, ruler of Germany until 1918; Helen's married name is Kaiser
3. True
4. C
5. "Skip to My Lou"

Quiz 139
1. With new seasickness pills and a "trial run" on the Staten Island Ferry
2. Five o'clock in the afternoon
3. Fall asleep
4. B
5. Ricky slaps Lucy in the face to wake her up so she can sign her passport application

Quiz 140
1. B
2. Her skirt gets caught in the chain of a bicycle
3. The pilot boat
4. A cigar

5. At Idlewild Airport (now J.F.K.)

Quiz 141
1. B
2. Ping-pong
3. *Noah's Ark*
4. Hamilton
5. The Boat 'n' Bottle Bar

Quiz 142
1. *Is Your Cocker Off His Rocker?*, *Is Your Poodle Off His Noodle?*, and *Is Your Collie Off His Trolley?*
2. A
3. She overpractices her curtsying.
4. "The Circus"
5. The strange British monetary system

Quiz 143
1. A
2. Acting
3. Danny
4. Lucy; she falls off her horse and into a bramble bush, which just happens to be inhabited by the fox
5. At Sir Clive's Berkshire Manor estate

Quiz 144
1. B
2. She has arrived just in time to be fed to a dragon
3. C
4. A Dragon's Dinner
5. Scotty MacTavish MacDougal MacCardo

Quiz 145
1. B
2. One thousand
3. She asks for catsup, then passes a counterpoint bill
4. Italian
5. The Hotel Royale

178

Quiz 146
1. At a sidewalk cafe
2. C
3. DuBois
4. Eating an orange
5. Art Buchwald's

Quiz 147
1. Marcel
2. B
3. Ricky wants to take Lucy's picture, but instead of the camera, finds a roast chicken in the camera bag
4. A horse's feedbag and an ice bucket
5. $500

Quiz 148
1. "La Cucaracha"
2. Lucy slams the cabin door
3. A
4. 24
5. Locarno

Quiz 149
1. B
2. Giuseppe
3. There is no operable elevator
4. False; it's Little Teresa
5. No. 47

Quiz 150
1. Vittorio Felipe
2. *Bitter*
3. B
4. True
5. Turo, Italy

Quiz 151
1. Nice
2. Jam
3. She cannot locate her passport and visa
4. A
5. 25

Quiz 152
1. The LeGrill restaurant in the casino

2. B
3. In Ethel's lingerie case
4. False; he finds it in Ethel's lingerie case
5. Her Aunt Yvette

Quiz 153
1. A
2. Lucy's airplane seat-mate; Evelyn
3. Chester
4. True
5. 66 pounds

Quiz 154
1. To talk him into appearing at Ricky's new club
2. A baseball hits him on the head
3. A baseball player
4. The Ump
5. A Cleveland Indians-New York Yankees game

Quiz 155
1. B
2. *Romeo and Juliet*
3. Hanna
4. Princess Loo-Cee, Welles's assistant in the magic act
5. She wants to buy skin-diving equipment for her trip to Florida

Quiz 156
1. False; the Ricardos and Mertzes discuss nervousness
2. B
3. Ricky
4. Reverse
5. Earl Robey

Quiz 157
1. She buys him a doctor's kit
2. A
3. 99
4. True
5. "Nurtz to the Mertz Mambo"

Quiz 158

1. Venice (he was their gondolier)
2. False; he has come to see his brother Dominic
3. B
4. His work permit is invalid
5. $10

Quiz 159

1. Lucy has misplaced the train tickets and neither she nor Ethel has enough money to buy replacements
2. Watercress
3. A
4. False; on a poultry truck
5. Evelyn Holmby

Quiz 160

1. B
2. That is the amount of money Lucy and Ethel have spent on a hotel boutique shopping spree
3. Tuna
4. False; Little Ricky caught one, then Ricky "caught" one
5. No. 919

Quiz 161

1. True
2. She instructs the dock attendant to fill the gas tank on their rented boat only halfway
3. Lucy intends to "save the day" by "discovering" a vacuum jug of gasoline
4. A film documentary about Florida is being shot
5. Claude Akins

Quiz 162

1. False; it is Uncle Alberto
2. B
3. Grandos
4. "Babalu"
5. At the Casino Parisien nightclub of the Hotel Nacional

Quiz 163

1. A hollow tree
2. B
3. She fits into the costume worn last year by Jimmy Wilson's mother
4. *Enchanted*
5. Clifford Terry

Quiz 164

1. Johnny Longden
2. True
3. A
4. With it still on Lucy's head, Ricky reads the inscription to the assembled crowd
5. Flatbush Avenue

Quiz 165

1. C
2. A new tenant in the Mertz building, Mr. Stewart, objects strenuously to the dog's yelping
3. Fred
4. Big grouch
5. Billy Palmer

Quiz 166

1. Both mothers plan to have birthday parties on the same Saturday and they have the same guest lists
2. Supermud
3. False; Ricky knows him
4. Two prospective tenants lock the window because they assume it will rain
5. 15

Quiz 167

1. True
2. A
3. Westport, Connecticut
4. "Brains"
5. Eleanor and Joe Spaulding

Quiz 168

1. Heebie-jeebies

2. B
3. Cut off its legs
4. The present owners' move has been delayed
5. The Taylors

Quiz 169
1. True
2. A basket of fruit
3. A
4. The Ricardos' phone has not been connected yet
5. $8.16

Quiz 170
1. A
2. A forty percent discount
3. Chinese Modern
4. Advertising agency
5. $3,272.75

Quiz 171
1. C
2. Lucy
3. Mrs. Trumbull's sister has agreed to move in and manage their building
4. Little Ricky leaves the door ajar
5. 500

Quiz 172
1. C
2. Six dozen
3. They have promised to perform at a PTA function
4. True
5. Six

Quiz 173
1. Lucy has promised his professional services for a Westport Historical Society benefit
2. Violin
3. "Sweet Sue"
4. Is Smarter
5. "She'll Be Comin' 'Round the Mountain"

Quiz 174
1. B
2. Lucy purchased tickets for a matinee, but thought they were for an evening performance
3. He has just collected the rents on the apartment building
4. Ricky is able to purchase only two new (box) seats to the current performance
5. 25

Quiz 175
1. They discover they were both born in Albuquerque, New Mexico
2. False; via an intercom Fred has installed
3. C
4. Thick as thieves
5. The Munsens, Baileys, and Ramseys

Quiz 176
1. Ricky's on a week's vacation and is bored
2. A
3. They start the job, hoping the boys will expect them to botch it and take over
4. It falls out of Ricky's shirt pocket into a platter of hamburger meat
5. They think that Ricky's old shirt, now part of Little Ricky's kite's tail, is flying high over the water

Quiz 177
1. A
2. Fred
3. Lucy dons a super-tight dress, Ethel has her hair done up like Grace Kelly, and Betty sports an exotic perfume
4. False; Pat Boone
5. Jordan

Quiz 178
1. "Best Looking Garden"
2. Betty Ramsey
3. He has gone to see a New York Yankees game
4. B
5. At the Village Gift Shop

Quiz 179
1. C
2. Town crier
3. Little Ricky announces that his dog has run away
4. Ricky
5. Mr. Sylvestri

Quiz 180
1. C
2. A
3. G
4. H
5. E
6. I
7. B
8. J
9. F
10. D

Quiz 181
1. Jerry, the agent
2. Mr. Jamison
3. A few of Ricky's band members
4. Ethel
5. Fred

Quiz 182
1. Ramon
2. Boo-shoo
3. 79
4. Out
5. Indianapolis

Quiz 183

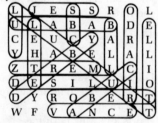

Quiz 184
1. Albuquerque, New Mexico

2. He operates a soda fountain
3. At the Mayo Brothers' clinic
4. Oscar; Emmy
5. May, Roberta, or Louise (depending on the episode)
6. Will Potter

Quiz 185
1. Hans Conreid
2. Mary Jane Croft
3. Frank Nelson
4. Jay Novello
5. Irving Bacon

Quiz 186
1. True
2. False
3. True
4. False; in an early episode, it is revealed he had five brothers
5. True
6. False; he loves baseball and boxing
7. True
8. False; we once met her nephew Joe, an appliance repairman, and the Mertzes mentioned that she had a sister
9. False
10. True

Quiz 187
1. "I Love Lucy and she loves me/We're as happy as two can be"
2. Friday
3. Esmeralda
4. A Big Hunk of America
5. $300
6. $50
7. Snails (escargot)
8. Her mother, Mrs. MacGillicuddy
9. "Buttered grass"
10. Isabella Klump and Lucille MacGillicuddy

Quiz 188
1. B
2. D
3. A
4. E
5. C

Quiz 189
1. Parker is not one of the Ricardos' doctors
2. Moore is not a tenant of the Mertz apartment building
3. Judith Applegate is not a member of the Wednesday Afternoon Fine Arts League
4. Van Johnson did not provide a Hollywood souvenir for Lucy
5. Rita Hayworth was not considered as Ricky's "Don Juan" co-star

Quiz 190
1. A
2. C
3. G
4. H
5. J
6. B
7. E
8. I
9. F
10. D

Quiz 191
1. 623 East 68th Street
2. $50
3. 23%
4. $100
5. 129 pounds

Quiz 192
1. Hobart
2. 1,153 jars
3. Acme Employment Agency
4. Pork chops, baked potato and asparagus tips with hollandaise sauce
5. Steubenville, Ohio

Quiz 193
1. Fred on the occasion of Ricky's re-showing his home movies
2. Ethel to Lucy when Lucy discovers she's gained too much weight
3. Hollywood tour bus driver to Lucy when she tells the busload of tourists that Ricky is having lunch with Richard Widmark
4. Lucy to Ethel when the pair is forced to wash dishes at an Italian restaurant because they haven't enough money to pay their checks
5. Ethel to Lucy when they encounter a flat tire on the way to Florida
6. Lucy to Marion Strong when the latter starts cackling
7. Lucy when asked if she told anyone about Ricky's impending *Don Juan* screen test
8. Fred when Little Ricky suddenly stops playing his new snare drum
9. Fred to Ethel when the latter lifts up her skirt in the courtroom battle over a TV set
10. Lucy to a movie director when Lucy ruins her chances for an on-screen role in a Hollywood movie